Heathkit
Educational Systems

MICROPROCESSORS

Student Workbook

Copyright © 1978
Twenty-first printing — 1983
EB-6401-40   595-2264-02

Heath Company Benton Harbor, Michigan 49022   *All Rights Reserved*
Not Affiliated With D.C. Heath Inc.
Printed in the United States of America

CONTENTS

Introduction

This Student Workbook contains 19 experiments, 10 programming experiments and 9 interfacing experiments.

You will perform each of the experiments using the ET-3400 Microprocessor Trainer. At the end of Units 1 through 6 in the textbook, you will be instructed to perform one or more of the programming experiments in the Workbook. The early programs are extremely simple. The later programs are more complex, but you will be able to accomplish them as you become familiar with the instruction set and programming techniques. Before you finish the texts, you will be writing programs that will turn the trainer into a clock, a musical instrument, a digital voltmeter, etc.

You will be instructed to perform the interfacing experiments at the end of Units 7 and 8. Most of the circuit parts for these experiments are supplied in the EB-6401-30 parts pack. The remaining parts are part of the Trainer.

The following schedule is suggested for performing the experiments.

Experiments 1 and 2	after Unit 1.
Experiment 3	after Unit 2.
Experiment 4	after Unit 3.
Experiments 5 and 6	after Unit 4.
Experiments 7 and 8	after Unit 5.
Experiments 9 and 10	after Unit 6.
Experiments 11, 12, 13 and 14	after Unit 7.
Experiments 15, 16, 17, 18 and 19	after Unit 8.

An examination for each unit is also included in this workbook.

PROGRAMMING EXPERIMENTS

Experiment 1

Binary/Decimal Training Program

OBJECTIVES:

To improve your ability to convert binary numbers to their decimal equivalent.

To improve your ability to convert decimal numbers to their binary equivalent.

To present the proper procedure for entering a program into the Microprocessor Trainer.

To demonstrate the versatility of the Microprocessor Trainer and microprocessors in general.

INTRODUCTION

In Unit 1, you were introduced to the binary number system. As you proceed through this course, you will find the need to convert binary numbers to decimal, and decimal numbers to binary. To improve your ability to make these conversions, you will enter a program into the Microprocessor Trainer to allow it to act as your instructor. In the first half of this experiment, you will use the Trainer to practice binary-to-decimal conversion.

When you use the Trainer, carefully follow all of the operating instructions. A microprocessor can only perform properly if it is programmed properly. However, you do not need programming experience at this time; just follow the instructions provided in this experiment. Do not worry about what you are entering.

The Trainer Manual contains a great amount of useful information in the Operation Section. You should review that section before you proceed with this experiment.

If your Trainer has been modified for use with the Heathkit Memory I/O Accessory, unplug the Trainer from the AC wall receptacle. Disconnect the 40-pin plug that connects the Trainer to the Memory I/O Accessory.

If your Trainer is Model number ET-3400, reinstall the 2112 RAM IC's at IC-14 through IC-17 before starting the experiments in this unit.

If your Trainer is Model number ET-3400A, reinstall the 2114 RAM IC's at IC-14 and IC-15 before starting the experiments in this unit.

PROCEDURE

1. Plug in the Trainer and push the POWER switch on. Then momentarily press the RESET key. The display should show CPU UP.

2. Push the AUTO (automatic) key. Displays H, I, N, and Z will show "prompt" characters (bottom segment of each digit illuminated), and displays V and C will show Ad. NOTE: The letters identifying each display are located near their bottom right corners.

3. Push the 0 key three times. 0's will appear in displays H, I; and N.

4. Push, but do not release the 0 key. A 0 will appear in display Z. Now release the key. The 0 will not change, but displays V and C will now show prompt characters.

   NOTE: The Trainer is now ready to receive program data. If you make a data error while entering the program, do not attempt to correct the error; continue programming. Any errors will be located and corrected when you examine your program.

ADDRESS	INST/DATA	ADDRESS	INST/DATA	ADDRESS	INST/DATA
0000	00*	0029	08	0052	00
0001	00*	002A	08	0053	3B
0002	BD	002B	00	0054	4F
0003	FC	002C	00	0055	DB
0004	BC	002D	00	0056	BD
0005	BD	002E	80	0057	00
0006	FE	002F	BD	0058	69
0007	52	0030	FC	0059	7E
0008	5E	0031	BC	005A	00
0009	FE	0032	BD	005B	02
000A	7C	0033	FE	005C	BD
000B	00	0034	09	005D	FE
000C	01	0035	97	005E	52
000D	B6	0036	00	005F	00
000E	CO	0037	BD	0060	00
000F	03	0038	00	0061	15
0010	01	0039	69	0062	9D
0011	46	003A	5F	0063	BD
0012	25	003B	84	0064	00
0013	F6	003C	FO	0065	69
0014	CE	003D	27	0066	7E
0015	00	003E	07	0067	00
0016	00	003F	80	0068	14
0017	DF	0040	10	0069	CE
0018	F2	0041	CB	006A	00
0019	BD	0042	OA	006B	00
001A	FD	0043	4D	006C	09
001B	93	0044	26	006D	26
001C	B6	0045	F9	006E	FD
001D	CO	0046	96	006F	96
001E	06	0047	00	0070	01
001F	01	0048	84	0071	84
0020	46	0049	0F	0072	3F
0021	25	004A	1B	0073	97
0022	F9	004B	90	0074	01
0023	BD	004C	01	0075	96
0024	FC	004D	26	0076	00
0025	BC	004E	OD	0077	39
0026	BD	004F	BD		RESET
0027	FE	0050	FE		
0028	52	0051	52		

*This data may change randomly.

Figure 1
Binary-to-decimal training program.

5. Using the Trainer keys, enter the Binary-to-Decimal training program shown in Figure 1. At each address specified, press the appropriate inst/data (program instruction or data) number keys (most significant number first). Displays V and C will show the inst/data word you have entered. Note that as you release the second data key, address displays H, I, N, and Z will increment (count up one), and displays V and C will again show prompt characters. When you get to the end of the program, press the RESET key as indicated.

6. Now that you have entered the Binary-to-Decimal training program, you must examine the data for errors. Use the following sequence to examine the data and correct any errors.

    A. Press the EXAM (examine) key. Note that the display is now asking for a 4-digit address (_ _ _ _ Ad.)

    B. Enter the beginning address of the program (0000). As soon as the last address digit is entered, displays V and C show the contents of that memory location. NOTE: The address is a memory location in the Trainer.

    C. Now compare the displayed address and data with the address and inst/data columns in the program.

    D. If the displayed data is incorrect, press the CHAN (change) key. The data displays will now show prompt characters. Enter the correct data.

    E. Press the FWD (forward) key. The address will increment and the data for that memory location will be shown. Correct the data if necessary.

    F. Continue to step through the program with the FWD key, and correct data as necessary, until you reach the end of the program. It is not necessary to examine or modify the memory beyond address 0077 since it will have no effect on the program.

7. Press the RESET key.

8. Press the DO key, then enter address 0002. The display should show GO. If the display shows a different number or word, or goes blank, your program contains an error. Repeat steps 6 through 8.

9. Press the F key. A 6-bit binary number should appear in the display. This is a random number and should change in value when you are told to "GO" next time.

10. Examine the binary number and determine its decimal value. Then press the D key. Two prompt characters should appear in the display.

11. Enter the decimal value of the binary number previously displayed (most significant digit first.) For values less than 10, enter a 0 before you enter the value. After approximately one second, the Trainer will indicate whether or not your answer is correct.

12. If your answer was correct, the Trainer will display YES. After approximately one second, the word GO will replace the decimal number.

    If your answer was incorrect, the Trainer will display NO. After approximately one second, the same binary number will again be displayed. Determine and enter the decimal value as described in steps 10 and 11.

13. Refer again to steps 9 through 12 and practice converting binary numbers to their decimal equivalent. You should obtain 10 correct answers in succession before you continue with this experiment.

DISCUSSION

Now that you have used the Trainer and its microprocessor, you have accomplished three objectives. First, you are becoming proficient in binary-to-decimal conversion. Second, you have been introduced to the correct method for entering, examining, and modifying a program. Third, you have been shown how a simple set of instructions can produce a powerful training aid. However, you should remember, a microprocessor can only perform what you tell it. One incorrect instruction can produce totally unexpected results.

Now, reprogram the Trainer for decimal-to-binary instruction. Since you will be using the same memory locations used in the first half of this experiment, the Binary-To-Decimal program will disappear.

PROCEDURE (Continued)

14. Press the RESET key.

15. Press the AUTO key, and enter address 0000.

16. Using the Trainer keys, enter the Decimal-to-Binary training program shown in Figure 2.

17. Now that you have entered the Decimal-to-Binary program, press the EXAM key and enter address 0000.

18. Using the FWD key, compare the Trainer memory contents with the program address and inst/data listing. If you must correct any data, press the CHAN key and enter the proper data.

19. After you have checked the program, press the RESET key.

20. Press the DO key, then enter address 0001. The display should show GO. If the display shows a different number or word, or goes blank, your program contains an error. Repeat steps 17 through 20.

21. Press the F key. A 2-digit decimal number should appear in the display, next to the word GO. This is a random number and should change in value when you are told to "GO" next time.

22. Examine the decimal number and determine its binary value. Then press the D key. Six prompt characters should appear in the display.

23. Enter the binary value of the decimal number previously displayed, beginning with the most significant bit (MSB). If the decimal value is less than 32, be sure to enter any leading zeros. NOTE: Although the program will accept any number combination, you should use only 1's and 0's.

ADDRESS	INST/DATA	ADDRESS	INST/DATA	ADDRESS	INST/DATA
0000	00*	002F	85	005E	00
0001	CE	0030	BD	005F	7E
0002	C1	0031	FD	0060	CE
0003	6F	0032	25	0061	C1
0004	BD	0033	4F	0062	3F
0005	FE	0034	E6	0063	BD
0006	50	0035	00	0064	FE
0007	5E	0036	C5	0065	50
0008	FE	0037	10	0066	00
0009	96	0038	27	0067	00
000A	00	0039	03	0068	80
000B	8B	003A	AB	0069	7E
000C	01	003B	03	006A	00
000D	19	003C	19	006B	01
000E	81	003D	56	006C	BD
000F	63	003E	24	006D	FE
0010	23	003F	03	006E	52
0011	01	0040	AB	006F	15
0012	4F	0041	06	0070	1D
0013	97	0042	19	0071	00
0014	00	0043	08	0072	00
0015	B6	0044	8C	0073	00
0016	CO	0045	00	0074	80
0017	03	0046	88	0075	BD
0018	01	0047	26	0076	00
0019	46	0048	EB	0077	7E
001A	25	0049	BD	0078	BD
001B	ED	004A	00	0079	FC
001C	96	004B	7E	007A	BC
001D	00	004C	BD	007B	7E
001E	BD	004D	FC	007C	00
001F	FE	004E	BC	007D	1C
0020	20	004F	D6	007E	CE
0021	B6	0050	00	007F	00
0022	CO	0051	11	0080	00
0023	06	0052	26	0081	09
0024	01	0053	18	0082	26
0025	46	0054	BD	0083	FD
0026	25	0055	FE	0084	39
0027	F9	0056	52	0085	00
0028	BD	0057	00	0086	00
0029	FC	0058	00	0087	00
002A	BC	0059	00	0088	32
002B	C6	005A	3B	0089	08
002C	03	005B	4F	008A	02
002D	CE	005C	DB	008B	16
002E	00	005D	BD	008C	04
				008D	01
					RESET

*This data may change randomly

Figure 2
Decimal-to-binary training program.

24. If your answer was correct, the Trainer will display YES approximately one second after you enter the last binary bit. Approximately one second later, the Trainer will display GO.

If your answer was incorrect, the Trainer will display NO approximately one second after you enter the last binary bit. Approximately one second later, the same decimal number will be displayed again. Determine and enter the binary value as described in steps 22 and 23.

25. Refer again to steps 21 through 24 and practice converting decimal numbers to their binary equivalent. You should obtain 10 correct answers in succession before you continue with this experiment.

DISCUSSION

In this half of the experiment, you were given further experience in programming with the ET-3400 Microprocessor Trainer. You also improved your ability to readily translate decimal numbers into binary. This ability will become very useful as you progress through the Microprocessor Course.

Experiment 2

Hexadecimal/Decimal Training Program

OBJECTIVES:

> To practice the conversion of decimal numbers to their hexadecimal equivalent.

> To practice the conversion of hexadecimal numbers to their decimal equivalent.

INTRODUCTION

Binary numbers are used in all microprocessors to represent data and instructions. But binary numbers are difficult to work with .... especially when the number contains 8_{10} bits or more. To simplify programming, microprocessor designers usually use other number systems, like octal or hexadecimal, to represent binary data. Both octal and hexadecimal are just shorthand notations of binary numbers. Although the numbers are entered in hexadecimal or octal, the microprocessor "sees" them as binary. This simplifies programming.

For example, the binary number 10011111_2 requires eight key closures for entry. Fortunately, this same number can be represented in hexadecimal as $9F_{16}$ and requires only two key closures for entry. Fewer key closures means less programming errors and more efficient programming.

Your Microprocessor Trainer is based on the hexadecimal number system. You probably noticed this when you loaded the programs in the previous experiment; all instructions were coded in hexadecimal. The Microprocessor Trainer normally displays data in hexadecimal form. Of course, special programs allow the Trainer to accept binary or decimal numbers, as you saw in the first experiment. However, these special programs waste a portion of the microprocessors potential power and aren't necessary because you can make the conversion from decimal to hexadecimal with a little practice. That's the purpose of this experiment. . . to sharpen your conversion skills.

Again, you will use the Microprocessor Trainer for this purpose. First, you'll enter a program that allows you to practice conversion from decimal to hexadecimal. Then you'll load the second program that reverses the process. You'll find that it's not as difficult as it might appear.

Now briefly review decimal-to-hexadecimal conversion. Initially, it's helpful to make up a chart of decimal numbers and their hexadecimal equivalents, as shown here.

DECIMAL	0	1	2	3	4	5	6	7	8	9	10	11	12	13	14	15
HEXADECIMAL	0	1	2	3	4	5	6	7	8	9	A	B	C	D	E	F

Recall that hexadecimal is a base 16_{10} number system. Both systems use identical numbers from 0 through 9. However, at decimal number 10, the hexadecimal system shifts to characters of the alphabet, as shown by the letters A through F. Conversion of a decimal number to it's hexadecimal equivalent is a simple process where the decimal number is repeatedly divided by 16_{10}, with the remainder producing the equivalent hexadecimal number. This example will use only 2-digit numbers, since that's what you'll be converting in this experiment.

Suppose you want to convert 92_{10} to hexadecimal. The first step is to divide 92_{10} by 16_{10} as shown below.

$$\begin{array}{r} 5 \\ 16\,\overline{)\,92} \\ -\,80 \\ \hline \end{array}$$

Remainder $\qquad 12_{10} = C_{16} \leftarrow$ LSD

The quotient is 5, but remember, we aren't concerned with this at the moment. We're interested in the remainder, in this case 12_{10}, because it forms the LSD of the equivalent hexadecimal number. Now, refer to the chart and find that $12_{10} = C_{16}$ and write this down as the LSD of the hex equivalent. The next step is to take the quotient of the previous division, in this case 5_{10}, and divide it by 16_{10}, as shown below.

$$\begin{array}{r} 0 \\ 16\,\overline{)\,5} \\ -\,0 \\ \hline \end{array}$$

Remainder $\rightarrow \qquad 5_{10} = 5_{16} \leftarrow$ MSD

Of course, the quotient of this division is 0, signifying that the remainder, 5_{10}, is the MSD of the hexadecimal number. Checking the chart, you find that $5_{10} = 5_{16}$. Combining the MSD (5_{16}) and LSD (C_{16}), you find that the hex equivalent of 92_{10} is $5C_{16}$. You'll find that, after you've made the conversion a few times, you'll be able to do them in your head. You'll get that practice in this experiment.

PROCEDURE

1.   Turn on the Trainer and press the RESET key.

2.   Press AUTO and then enter address 0000.

3.   Now enter the Decimal-to-Hexadecimal training program, shown in Figure 3, into the Trainer. When you've entered the last program instruction press the RESET key as shown at the end of the program.

ADDRESS	INST/DATA	ADDRESS	INST/DATA	ADDRESS	INST/DATA	ADDRESS	INST/DATA
0000	00*	0024	BD	0048	52	006C	00
0001	CE	0025	FE	0049	00	006D	00
0002	C1	0026	52	004A	3B	006E	00
0003	6F	0027	08	004B	4F	006F	00
0004	BD	0028	08	004C	DB	0070	00
0005	FE	0029	00	004D	BD	0071	80
0006	50	002A	00	004E	00	0072	39
0007	5E	002B	00	004F	63		RESET
0008	FE	002C	80	0050	7E		
0009	96	002D	BD	0051	00		
000A	00	002E	FC	0052	01		
000B	8B	002F	BC	0053	BD		
000C	01	0030	BD	0054	FE		
000D	19	0031	FE	0055	52		
000E	97	0032	09	0056	00		
000F	00	0033	36	0057	00		
0010	B6	0034	4F	0058	15		
0011	CO	0035	D6	0059	9D		
0012	03	0036	00	005A	BD		
0013	46	0037	CO	005B	00		
0014	25	0038	10	005C	63		
0015	F3	0039	25	005D	BD		
0016	96	003A	04	005E	FC		
0017	00	003B	8B	005F	BC		
0018	BD	003C	OA	0060	7E		
0019	FE	003D	20	0061	00		
001A	20	003E	F8	0062	16		
001B	B6	003F	CB	0063	CE		
001C	CO	0040	10	0064	00		
001D	06	0041	1B	0065	00		
001E	46	0042	33	0066	09		
001F	25	0043	11	0067	26		
0020	FA	0044	26	0068	FD		
0021	BD	0045	OD	0069	BD		
0022	FC	0046	BD	006A	FD		
0023	BC	0047	FE	006B	8D		

* This data may change randomly

Figure 3
Decimal-to-hexadecimal training program.

4. Check the stored program by first pressing the EXAM key and then entering address 0000. Now use the FWD key to step through the program, comparing the contents of memory with the program in Figure 3. Remember, the four left-most digits of the display represent the memory address and the two digits at the right are the contents of memory that should correspond with the INST/DATA listing of the program. If you find a mistake, correct it by first pressing the CHAN key and then entering the proper data.

5. When you're satisfied that the program is correct, press the RESET key.

6. Now it's time to execute the program. Do this by pressing the DO key and then entering address 0001. The word "GO" should now appear in the two left-most digits. If the display is blank, or if other numbers or letters appear, there is an error in the program and steps 4 and 5 should be repeated.

7. Now press the F key. A 2-digit "decimal" number will appear on the display. The Trainer is asking you to convert this decimal number to its hexadecimal equivalent. Therefore, examine the decimal number and then convert it to hexadecimal.

8. Enter your answer by first pressing key D. Two prompt characters will appear in the left-most digits. Now enter your hexadecimal number.

    If you respond correctly, the Trainer will display "YES" for a short period and then give you another "GO." Pressing the F key will cause another random number to be displayed.

    An incorrect response will result in the word "NO" on the display. After a short delay, the original decimal number will reappear and you should try the conversion process again. This cycle continues until you arrive at the correct answer.

9. Repeat steps 7 and 8, practicing conversion until you're confident of your ability. A good guideline to follow is . . . . when you answer 10 consecutive queries correctly, you're probably proficient.

DISCUSSION

As you worked through the exercises in this experiment, you probably developed your own shorthand method of conversion. After a few queries, you probably found that you didn't need the decimal-to-hexadecimal conversion chart any longer . . . you had the chart committed to memory. Perhaps you noticed that when 16_{10} is divided into the 2-digit decimal numbers used in this experiment, the resulting quotient always equals the MSD of the hexadecimal equivalent. Naturally, the remainder is the LSD. However, this only works for decimal numbers less than 159_{10}. For larger numbers, the procedure studied earlier must be used.

Since the Microprocessor Trainer displays data in hexadecimal and we naturally think in decimal, the conversion process must be reversed to interpret output data from the Trainer. For example, if the Trainer is programmed to add the numbers $1A_{16}$ and $9B_{16}$, the result $B5_{16}$ will be displayed. This hexadecimal number means very little. To understand the result, you must convert the sum ($B5_{16}$) to its decimal equivalent (181_{10}). Now the answer is clear.

Several methods can be used to change hexadecimal numbers to decimal. One process uses double conversion; first, the hexadecimal number is reduced to its binary equivalent; next, the resulting binary number is transformed into the resulting decimal equivalent.

Another, more commonly used method, is to use positional notation, inherent in any number system, and multiply each digit by its weighted value and then add the products. For example, the decimal equivalent of the hex number 11_{16} is derived as shown below:

$$\text{Assign Weights:} \quad 16^1 \qquad\qquad 16^0 \quad \text{Positional Weights}$$
$$1 \qquad\qquad\quad 1$$

Weight × Digit: $1 \times 16^1 = 16 \longleftarrow\!\!\rfloor \qquad \lfloor\!\!\longrightarrow 1 \times 16^0 = 1$

Add Products: $\qquad\qquad\qquad 16 + 1 = 17$

Final Result: $\qquad\qquad\qquad 11_{16} = 17_{10}$

The first step is to assign positioned weights to each digit. Since the number is hexadecimal, each position represents a power of 16_{10}. Next, multiply each digit by its positional weight. Finally, add the products. The resulting sum is the decimal equivalent. Therefore, as shown in the example, 11_{16} is equal to 17_{10}.

Now try a problem that's a bit more difficult . . . converting $6B_{16}$ to decimal. To begin with, this expression hardly looks like a number. Instead, it's a combination of a number and a letter. However, the notation at the bottom of the expression denotes a base 16 number so we know it's hexadecimal. The translation process is almost identical to the previous example. The only difference being that the hexadecimal "letter" must be changed to decimal before it can be multiplied by the positional weight. The conversion process is shown below.

Assign Weights: $\qquad\qquad\qquad\quad 16^1 \qquad 16^0$

$\qquad\qquad\qquad\qquad\qquad\qquad\quad 6 \qquad\;\; B$

Convert to Decimal: $6_{16} = 6_{10}\; \longleftarrow \qquad \longrightarrow B_{16} = 11_{10}$

Weight × Digit: $\qquad 6 \times 16^1 = 96 \qquad\quad 11 \times 16^0 = 11$

Add Products: $\qquad\qquad\quad 96 + 11 = 107$

Final Result: $\qquad\qquad\quad 6B_{16} = 107_{10}$

Again, we begin by assigning positional weights to each digit. However, now the second step is to convert the hexadecimal characters to decimal numbers. Recall that 6_{16} is equal to 6_{10} and that B_{16} equals 11_{10}. Now multiply the weight by the decimal numbers, add the products and obtain the final result. As shown, the decimal equivalent of $6B_{16}$ is 107_{10}.

In the next section of this experiment, you will load a hexadecimal-to-decimal training program in the Trainer and then practice hexadecimal-to-decimal conversion.

PROCEDURE (Continued)

10. Prepare to enter the new program by pressing the RESET key. Next press the AUTO key and then enter address 0000.

11. Refer to Figure 4 and enter the Hexadecimal-to-Decimal training program listed there. When you've entered all of the instructions, press the RESET key as indicated at the end of the program.

12. Check the program that you've loaded by pressing the EXAM key and then entering address 0000. Use the FWD key to step through the program, comparing the stored program with the program listing in Figure 4. Use the CHAN key to correct any errors that you find.

    When you are satisfied that the program is correct, press the RESET key.

13. Now execute the program by first pressing the DO key and then entering address 0001. The word "GO" should appear on the display. The absence of this word indicates a programming error and you should go back and recheck the program as outlined in step 12.

14. Now press the F key. A 2-digit "hexadecimal" number will appear. The Trainer is asking for the decimal equivalent of this number. Convert the hexadecimal number into its decimal equivalent. Then enter your answer by pressing the D key. Two prompt characters will appear. Now enter your answer.

    If your response is correct, the Trainer will display "YES." You can then continue these conversion exercises by again pressing the F key.

    However, if your answer is incorrect, the Trainer will display "NO." After a short delay, the original hexadecimal number will reappear, and you can try again.

15. Continue the conversion training program until you are confident of your ability to change hexadecimal numbers to decimal numbers. The standard of ten correct conversions in a row is a good guideline.

ADDRESS	INST/DATA	ADDRESS	INST/DATA	ADDRESS	INST/DATA	ADDRESS	INST/DATA
0000	00	0024	BD	0048	FE	006C	8D
0001	CE	0025	FC	0049	52	006D	00
0002	C1	0026	BC	004A	00	006E	00
0003	6F	0027	BD	004B	3B	006F	00
0004	BD	0028	FE	004C	4F	0070	00
0005	FE	0029	52	004D	DB	0071	00
0006	50	002A	08	004E	BD	0072	80
0007	5E	002B	08	004F	00	0073	39
0008	FE	002C	00	0050	64		RESET
0009	96	002D	00	0051	7E		
000A	00	002E	00	0052	00		
000B	4C	002F	80	0053	01		
000C	81	0030	BD	0054	BD		
000D	63	0031	FC	0055	FE		
000E	23	0032	BC	0056	52		
000F	01	0033	BD	0057	00		
0010	4F	0034	FE	0058	00		
0011	97	0035	09	0059	15		
0012	00	0036	5F	005A	9D		
0013	B6	0037	80	005B	BD		
0014	CO	0038	10	005C	00		
0015	03	0039	25	005D	64		
0016	46	003A	04	005E	BD		
0017	25	003B	CB	005F	FC		
0018	FO	003C	OA	0060	BC		
0019	96	003D	20	0061	7E		
001A	00	003E	F8	0062	00		
001B	BD	003F	8B	0063	19		
001C	FE	0040	10	0064	CE		
001D	20	0041	1B	0065	00		
001E	B6	0042	D6	0066	00		
001F	CO	0043	00	0067	09		
0020	06	0044	11	0068	26		
0021	46	0045	26	0069	FD		
0022	25	0046	OD	006A	BD		
0023	FA	0047	BD	006B	FD		

Figure 4

Hexadecimal-to-decimal training program.

DISCUSSION

The translation of hexadecimal numbers into decimal equivalent numbers is an important part of your training.

You will find this skill is extremely handy when you begin to write programs later in this course. Now you should be able to convert between hexadecimal and decimal numbers with ease. Perhaps you even developed your own shorthand methods for these translations. If so, use them. However, a word of caution . . . be sure they work for all numbers. As mentioned previously, some techniques work with small numbers, but not with large numbers.

Experiment 3

Straight Line Programs

OBJECTIVES:

To demonstrate the instructions presented in Unit 2 with simple programs.

To present three new instructions and use them in simple programs.

To demonstrate some programming pitfalls.

To demonstrate the difference between RAM and ROM.

INTRODUCTION

Unit 2 introduced you to the basic microprocessor and its internal structure. You also learned six basic microprocessor instructions that are represented by 8-bit binary numbers called "op codes." Op codes allow you to use the microprocessor for data manipulation. Figure 5 lists the six instructions and their op codes. It also lists three new instructions that you will use in this experiment. These new instructions use the inherent addressing mode described in Unit 2.

This is the first experiment to introduce microprocessor instructions that you can identify. There are a number of Trainer keyboard commands that you must learn in order to examine and use the microprocessor instructions. The Trainer commands that you should know for this experiment are:

DO — Execute the program, beginning at the address specified after this key is pressed.

EXAM (examine) — Display the address and memory contents at the address specified after this key is pressed. Memory contents can be changed by pressing the CHAN key and entering new data.

FWD (forward) — Advance to the next memory location and display the contents.

CHAN (change) — Open the memory location being examined so that new data can be entered.

NAME	MNEMONIC	OPCODE	DESCRIPTION
Load Accumulator (Immediate)	LDA	$1000\ 0110_2$ or 86_{16}	Load the contents of the next memory location into the accumulator.
Add (Immediate)	ADD	$1000\ 1011_2$ or $8B_{16}$	Add the contents of the next memory location to the present contents of the accumulator. Place the sum in the accumulator.
Load Accumulator (Direct)	LDA	$1001\ 0110_2$ or 96_{16}	Load the contents of the memory location whose address is given by the next byte into the accumulator.
Add (Direct)	ADD	$1001\ 1011_2$ or $9B_{16}$	Add the contents of the memory location whose address is given by the next byte to the present contents of the accumulator. Place the sum in the accumulator.
Store Accumulator (Direct)	STA	$1001\ 0111_2$ or 97_{16}	Store the contents of the accumulator in the memory location whose address is given by the next byte.
Halt (Inherent)	HLT	$0011\ 1110_2$ or $3E_{16}$	Stop all operations.
Clear Accumulator (Inherent)	CLRA	$0100\ 1111_2$ or $4F_{16}$	Reset all bits in the accumulator to 0.
Increment Accumulator (Inherent)	INCA	$0100\ 1100_2$ or $4C_{16}$	Add 1 to the contents of the accumulator.
Decrement Accumulator (Inherent)	DECA	$0100\ 1010_2$ or $4A_{16}$	Subtract 1 from the contents of the accumulator.

Figure 5

Instructions used in Experiment 3.

BACK — Go back to the previous memory location and display the contents.

AUTO (automatic) — Open the memory location specified, after this key is pressed, so that data can be entered. After data has been entered, automatically advance to the next memory location and wait for data.

SS (single step) — Go to the address specified by the program counter and execute the instruction at that address. Wait at the next instruction.

ACCA (accumulator) — Display the contents of the accumulator when this key is pressed. Accumulator contents can be changed by pressing the CHAN key and entering new data.

PC (program counter) — Display the contents of the program counter. This points to the next location in memory that the microprocessor will "fetch" from. Program counter contents can be changed by pressing the CHAN key and entering the new address.

RESET — Clear any Trainer keyboard commands and display "CPU UP." Memory contents and microprocessor contents are not disturbed.

You have access to all of these keyboard commands after the RESET key is pressed.

In this experiment, you will load some simple straight-line programs into the Trainer and examine how the microprocessor executes them. In its normal mode of operation, the microprocessor executes programs much too fast for a person to follow. It can execute hundreds of thousands of instructions each second. To allow us to witness the operation of the MPU, this high speed operation must be slowed down. The Microprocessor Trainer has a mode of operation that allows us to control the execution of single instructions. In this single-step mode, we can look at the contents of the accumulator, the program counter, and various memory locations, after each instruction is executed. In this way, we can follow exactly how the computer performs each step of the program. For this reason, you will use the single-step mode for most of the programs in this experiment.

PROCEDURE

1. Switch your Trainer on, and press the RESET key.

2. Your first program will use the immediate addressing mode to add two numbers. Press AUTO and enter starting address 0000. Then load the hex contents of the program listed in Figure 6.

HEX ADDRESS	HEX CONTENTS	MNEMONICS/ CONTENTS	COMMENTS
0000	86	LDA	Load accumulator immediately with
0001	21	33_{10}	Operand 1.
0002	8B	ADD	Add to accumulator immediately with
0003	17	23_{10}	Operand 2.
0004	3E	HLT	Stop.

Figure 6
Addition of two numbers through the
immediate addressing mode.

3. Press the RESET key, then examine your program to make sure it was properly entered. **Always** examine your program after it is entered.

4. Press the ACCA key and record the value _ _. This is a random number since no data has been loaded.

5. Press the PC key, then change the contents of the program counter to 0000 (the starting address of your program).

6. Press the SS key. This lets the Trainer execute the first instruction. The display should show 00028b. 0002 represents the address of the next instruction; 8b is the next instruction.

7. Press the ACCA key and record the value _ _. The first program instruction was LDA, and the next byte contained the data (operand) to be loaded, which is 21_{16}. This should be the value you recorded in this step.

8. Press the PC key and record the value _ _ _ _. This value points to the next memory location, which should be 0002.

You may have noted that the address 0002 and instruction 8b were displayed when you first pressed the SS key. This would seem to indicate that 8b was already fetched and the program counter should point to address 0003. However, the control program allows the Trainer to "look" at the next instruction.

9. Press the SS key and record the value _ _ _ _ _ _. The second instruction has been executed and the display should show the next instruction and its address.

10. Press the ACCA key and record the value _ _. The second operand has been added to the first operand and the sum is stored in the accumulator.

11. Press the SS key. Note that the display does not change. This is because the next instruction was a halt instruction ($3E_{16}$). The Trainer is preprogrammed to stop at a halt instruction. It also loses control of the single-step function when the halt instruction is implemented.

12. Enter the program (HEX contents) listed in Figure 7. Then examine the program to make sure it is properly entered.

HEX ADDRESS	HEX CONTENTS	MNEMONICS/ CONTENTS	COMMENTS
0000	96	LDA	Load accumulator direct with
0001	07	07_{16}	operand 1 which is stored at this address.
0002	9B	ADD	Add to accumulator direct with operand 2
0003	08	08_{16}	which is stored at this address.
0004	97	STA	Store the sum
0005	09	09_{16}	at this address.
0006	3E	HLT	Stop.
0007	20	32_{10}	Operand 1.
0008	17	23_{10}	Operand 2.
0009	00	00	Reserved for sum.

Figure 7

Additional of two numbers through the
direct addressing mode.

13. Press the ACCA key and record the value _ _. This is the value obtained in the previous program, a value you entered prior to this program, or a random value produced when you plugged in the Trainer.

14. Enter the program starting address into the program counter and single-step through the program. Record the specified information after each step.

   Step 1 display _ _ _ _ _ _.

   ACCA _ _.

   Step 2 display _ _ _ _ _ _.

   ACCA _ _.

   Step 3 display _ _ _ _ _ _.

   ACCA_ _.

15. Examine address 0009. Its value is _ _. This value should be identical to the value now stored in the ACCA.

16. Now compare your recorded data with the program in Figure 7. This will give you a general picture of how the microprocessor uses various instructions and data to perform a desired function.

17. Change the data in the ACCA and at address 0009 to FF, then execute the program with the DO key. This is done by depressing the DO key and then entering the address of the first instruction (0000). This allows the MPU to execute the program at its normal speed. After the program runs, you must press RESET to return control to the keyboard.

18. The data in the ACCA is _ _ and the data in address 0009 is _ _. These should be the same and equal to the sum of the two operands.

19. The program counter contains the address _ _ _ _. This should be the address of the next memory location after the HLT instruction.

20. Now write a program of your own. Using the **direct** addressing mode, write a program that will multiply 4 times 4, by adding 4 to itself in three consecutive steps. The final answer should be held in the accumulator. After you write your program, enter it into the Trainer and execute it. Keep trying until it produces a final result of 10_{16} (which is 16_{10}) in the accumulator.

One solution to the problem is shown in Figure 8. Yours should be similar, although not necessarily identical.

HEX ADDRESS	HEX CONTENTS	MNEMONICS/DECIMAL CONTENTS	COMMENTS
0000	96	LDA	Load accumulator direct with
0001	09	09_{16}	operand 1 which is stored at this address.
0002	9B	ADD	Add to accumulator direct with
0003	09	09_{16}	operand 1 which is stored at this address.
0004	9B	ADD	Add to accumulator direct with
0005	09	09_{16}	operand 1 which is stored at this address.
0006	9B	ADD	Add to accumulator direct with
0007	09	09_{16}	operand 1 which is stored at this address.
0008	3E	HLT	Stop.
0009	04	04_{10}	Operand 1.

Figure 8

Multiplication of a number by another through multiple addition in the direct addressing mode.

21. Load the program shown in Figure 8 into the Trainer. Enter the program starting address into the program counter and single-step through the program. Record the specified information after each step.

Step 1 display _ _ _ _ _ _.   ACCA _ _.

Step 2 display _ _ _ _ _ _.   ACCA _ _.

Step 3 display _ _ _ _ _ _.   ACCA _ _.

Step 4 display _ _ _ _ _ _.   ACCA _ _.

22. According to the microprocessor, the product of 4_{16} times 4_{16} is _ _$_{16}$.

23. Now that you are becoming acquainted with the instructions described in Unit 2, examine the three instructions introduced in this Experiment. Enter the program listed in Figure 9.

HEX ADDRESS	HEX CONTENTS	MNEMONICS/ CONTENTS	COMMENTS
0000	4F	CLRA	Clear accumulator.
0001	97	STA	Store the contents
0002	OA	OA_{16}	at this address.
0003	4C	INCA	Increment accumulator.
0004	97	STA	Store the contents
0005	OB	OB_{16}	at this address.
0006	4A	DECA	Decrement accumulator.
0007	97	STA	Store the contents
0008	OC	OC_{16}	at this address.
0009	3E	HLT	Stop.
000A	FF	FF_{16}	Reserved for data.
000B	FF	FF_{16}	Reserved for data.
000C	FF	FF_{16}	Reserved for data.

Figure 9
Implementation of the Clear, Increment,
and Decrement instructions.

24. Set the program counter to 0000 and single-step through the program. Record the specified information after each step.

Step 1 display _ _ _ _ _ _.   ACCA _ _.

Step 2 display _ _ _ _ _ _.   ACCA _ _.

Step 3 display _ _ _ _ _ _.   ACCA _ _.

Step 4 display _ _ _ _ _ _.   ACCA _ _.

Step 5 display _ _ _ _ _ _.   ACCA _ _.

Step 6 display _ _ _ _ _ _.

25. Compare your accumulated data with the program in Figure 9. Note that when op codes $4F_{16}$, $4C_{16}$, and $4A_{16}$ are executed, the single-step display advances only one address location. This is because of their inherent addressing mode; immediate and direct addressing modes require two locations in memory.

26. Shown below is a program to swap the contents of two memory locations. Now examine the process using the Trainer. Enter the program listed in Figure 10.

HEX ADDRESS	HEX CONTENTS	MNEMONICS/ CONTENTS	COMMENTS
0000	96	LDA	Load accumulator direct with operand 1
0001	10	10_{16}	stored at this address.
0002	97	STA	Store operand 1
0003	12	12_{16}	at this address.
0004	96	LDA	Load accumulator direct with operand 2
0005	11	11_{16}	stored at this address.
0006	97	STA	Store operand 2
0007	10	10_{16}	at this address.
0008	96	LDA	Load accumulator direct with operand 1
0009	12	12_{16}	stored at this address.
000A	97	STA	Store operand 1
000B	11	11_{16}	at this address.
000C	4F	CLRA	Clear the accumulator.
000D	97	STA	Store the contents
000E	12	12_{16}	at this address.
000F	3E	HLT	Stop.
0010	AA	170_{10}	Operand 1.
0011	BB	187_{10}	Operand 2.
0012	00	00	Temporary storage.

Figure 10
Data transfer between two addresses.

27. Set the program counter to starting address 0000 and single-step through the program. Record the specified information after each step.

        Step 1 display _ _ _ _ _ _.   ACCA _ _.

        Step 2 display _ _ _ _ _ _.   ACCA _ _.

        Step 3 display _ _ _ _ _ _.   ACCA _ _.

        Step 4 display _ _ _ _ _ _.   ACCA _ _.

        Step 5 display _ _ _ _ _ _.   ACCA _ _.

        Step 6 display _ _ _ _ _ _.   ACCA _ _.

        Step 7 display _ _ _ _ _ _.   ACCA _ _.

        Step 8 display _ _ _ _ _ _.   ACCA _ _.

28. Examine address:

        0010 _ _.

        0011 _ _.

        0012 _ _.

29. Compare your accumulated data with the program in Figure 10.

30. Now you will examine some common programming pitfalls. Without modifying the previous program, except as directed in Figure 11, enter the program listed in Figure 11.

HEX ADDRESS	HEX CONTENTS	MNEMONICS/ CONTENTS	COMMENTS
0000	86	LDA	Load accumulator immediately with
0001	4F	79_{10}	operand 1.
0002	97	STA	Store operand 1
0003	05	05_{16}	at this address.
0004	4A	DECA	Decrement accumulator
0005	3E	HLT	Stop.

Figure 11
Storing data at an address in the program.

31. Set the program counter to 0000 and single-step through the program. Record the specified information after each step.

Step 1 display _ _ _ _ _ _.   ACCA _ _.

Step 2 display _ _ _ _ _ _.   ACCA _ _.

Step 3 display _ _ _ _ _ _.   ACCA _ _.

Step 4 display _ _ _ _ _ _.   ACCA _ _.

Step 5 display _ _ _ _ _ _.   ACCA _ _.

Step 6 display _ _ _ _ _ _.   ACCA _ _.

Step 7 display _ _ _ _ _ _.   ACCA _ _.

Step 8 display _ _ _ _ _ _.   ACCA _ _.

Step 9 display _ _ _ _ _ _.   ACCA _ _.

32.   Compare your accumulated data with the program in Figure 11. Note that the data in the accumulator (operand 1) has been stored at address 0005. This removed the HLT instruction and allowed the microprocessor to continue executing any valid instructions in memory. In this case, the remaining unaltered instructions from the previous program are used. When you write a program, **make sure** you do not store data at an address that contains a needed instruction or data.

33.   Using the data you accumulated in step 31 of this experiment, plus the programs listed in Figures 10 and 11, determine the contents of address:

  0010 _ _.

  0011 _ _.

  0012 _ _.

34.   Now examine the Trainer contents at address:

  0010 _ _.

  0011 _ _.

  0012 _ _.

Your estimated data from step 33, and the actual contents should be identical. If they are not, re-examine your calculations and the contents of each memory location from 0000 to 0012. You might have inadvertently modified the contents of an address in the previous steps.

35. Without modifying the previous program, except as directed in Figure 12, enter the program listed in Figure 12.

HEX ADDRESS	HEX CONTENTS	MNEMONICS/ CONTENTS	COMMENTS
0000	86	LDA	Load accumulator immediately with
0001	40	64_{10}	operand 1.
0002	8B	ADD	Add to accumulator immediately with
0003	0A	10_{10}	operand 2.
0004	97	STA	Store the sum
0005	07	07_{16}	at this address.
0006	4F	CLRA	Clear accumulator.
0007	00	00	Reserved for data.

Figure 12
Addition of two numbers with immediate
addressing.

36. Set the program counter to 0000 and single-step through the program. Record the specified information after each step.

Step 1 display _ _ _ _ _ _.   ACCA _ _.

Step 2 display _ _ _ _ _ _.   ACCA _ _.

Step 3 display _ _ _ _ _ _.   ACCA _ _.

Step 4 display _ _ _ _ _ _.   ACCA _ _.

Step 5 display _ _ _ _ _ _.   ACCA _ _.

Step 6 display _ _ _ _ _ _.   ACCA _ _.

Step 7 display _ _ _ _ _ _.   ACCA _ _.

Step 8 display _ _ _ _ _ _.   ACCA _ _.

Step 9 display _ _ _ _ _ _.   ACCA _ _.

37. Compare your accumulated data with the program in Figure 12. Note that the Trainer executed the instructions beyond address 0007. This occurred because there was no halt instruction in the program. Always end your program with a halt instruction. If you don't, the microprocessor will try to execute all of the information contained in memory, thinking it is part of the program. In the process, the program you entered may get modified.

38. This final programming pitfall illustrates a problem almost everybody experiences. Enter the program listed in Figure 13.

HEX ADDRESS	HEX CONTENTS	MNEMONICS/ CONTENTS	COMMENTS
0000	96	LDA	Load accumulator direct with
0001	07	07_{16}	operand 1 stored at this address.
0002	8B	ADD	Add to accumulator direct with
0003	07	07_{16}	operand 1 stored at this address.
0004	8B	ADD	Add to accumulator direct with
0005	07	07_{16}	operand 1 stored at this address.
0006	3E	HLT	Stop.
0007	05	05_{10}	Operand 1.

Figure 13
Multiplication of two numbers using successive addition in the direct addressing mode.

39. Set the program counter to 0000 and single-step through the program. Record the specified information after each step.

Step 1 display _ _ _ _ _ _.   ACCA _ _.

Step 2 display _ _ _ _ _ _.   ACCA _ _.

Step 3 display _ _ _ _ _ _.   ACCA _ _.

40. Compare your accumulated data with the program in Figure 13. The program should have added 05 three times (5 × 3) for the answer OF. The Trainer indicates the answer is 13. This discrepancy occurred because the program contains the wrong **addressing mode op code** for the ADD function. It should be 9B rather than 8B. Return to Figure 13 and change the two ADD op codes to 9B so the program will be correct.

41. In Unit 2, you were shown that RAM (random access memory) was a read/write type memory, while ROM (read only memory) is a preprogrammed memory that can only be read and not written into. To examine these memory types, enter FF at address 0000 through 000F.

42. Examine the following memory locations and write down the contents next to each address. Use the first data column for each address. You will use the second column later.

ADDRESS	DATA	DATA	ADDRESS	DATA	DATA
0000	--	--	FD00	--	--
0001	--	--	FD01	--	--
0002	--	--	FD02	--	--
0003	--	--	FD03	--	--
0004	--	--	FD04	--	--
0005	--	--	FD05	--	--
0006	--	--	FD06	--	--
0007	--	--	FD07	--	--
0008	--	--	FD08	--	--
0009	--	--	FD09	--	--
000A	--	--	FD0A	--	--
000B	--	--	FD0B	--	--
000C	--	--	FD0C	--	--
000D	--	--	FD0D	--	--
000E	--	--	FD0E	--	--
000F	--	--	FD0F	--	--

43. Turn the Trainer power off, then unplug the line cord. Wait twenty seconds, then plug in the line cord and turn on the Trainer.

44. Examine the memory locations listed in step 42, and write down the contents next to each address, in the second data column. Compare the two sets of data. Notice the data obtained at address 0000 through 000F changed when all Trainer power was removed. However, the data at address FD00 through FD0F is unchanged. Address 0000 is RAM, while address FD00 is ROM. Memory is lost from RAM when power is removed. When power is reapplied, random data will appear in the memory.

    Enter FF at address FD00 through FD0F. Now examine address FD00 through FD0F. Notice the data is identical to that obtained in step 42. This shows that ROM can not be written into. You can send data down the data bus, but the memory will not accept it.

SUGGESTION: Use the nine instructions presented and write a few sample programs of your own. It's quite simple and can be great fun.

Experiment 4

Arithmetic and Logic Instructions

OBJECTIVES:

To present seven new instructions and use them in simple programs.

To demonstrate 2's complement conversion.

To demonstrate binary subtraction.

To demonstrate binary addition of signed numbers.

To demonstrate logical manipulation of data using the AND and OR instructions.

INTRODUCTION

In Experiment 3, you used nine instructions to write various programs. These instructions were:

MNEMONIC	OP CODE	ADDRESSING MODE
LDA	86_{16}	Immediate
LDA	96_{16}	Direct
ADD	$8B_{16}$	Immediate
ADD	$9B_{16}$	Direct
STA	97_{16}	Direct
CLRA	$4F_{16}$	Inherent
INCA	$4C_{16}$	Inherent
DECA	$4A_{16}$	Inherent
HLT	$3E_{16}$	Inherent

Seven new instructions are presented in this experiment. Each is listed in Figure 14.

Unit 3 examined the process of binary arithmetic, 2's complement arithmetic, signed number addition, and Boolean logic. Through sample programs, this experiment will illustrate some of the operations presented in Unit 3.

NAME	MNEMONIC	OPCODE	DESCRIPTION
Complement 2's or Negate (Inherent)	NEGA	$0100\ 0000_2$ or 40_{16}	Replace the contents of the accumulator with its complement plus 1.
Subtract (Immediate)	SUB	$1000\ 0000_2$ or 80_{16}	Subtract the contents of the next memory location from the contents of the accumulator. Place the difference in the accumulator.
Subtract (Direct)	SUB	$1001\ 0000_2$ or 90_{16}	Subtract the contents of the memory location whose address is given by the next byte from the present contents of the accumulator. Place the difference in the accumulator.
AND (Immediate)	ANDA	$1000\ 0100_2$ or 84_{16}	Perform the logical AND between the contents of the accumulator and the contents of the next memory location. Place the result in the accumulator.
AND (Direct)	ANDA	$1001\ 0100_2$ or 94_{16}	Perform the logical AND between the contents of the accumulator and the contents of the memory location whose address is given by the next byte. Place the result in the accumulator.
OR, Inclusive (Immediate)	ORA	$1000\ 1010_2$ or $8A_{16}$	Perform the logical OR between the contents of the accumulator and the contents of the next memory location. Place the result in the accumulator.
OR, Inclusive (Direct)	ORA	$1001\ 1010_2$ or $9A_{16}$	Perform the logical OR between the contents of the accumulator and the contents of the memory location whose address is given by the next byte. Place the result in the accumulator.

Figure 14
Instructions introduced in this experiment.

PROCEDURE

1. In the first part of the experiment, you will determine how the microprocessor represents negative and positive numbers. The program shown in Figure 15 loads a positive number into the accumulator and then repeatedly decrements the number until it is negative. Enter this program into the Trainer. Verify that you entered it properly by examining each address.

2. Go to the single-step mode by: pressing the PC key; pressing the CHAN key; and entering the starting address (0000). Single-step through the program by repeatedly pressing the SS key. Notice that the first instruction places $+5_{10}$ in the accumulator. Refer to Figure 16 and record the contents of the accumulator (in both hexadecimal and binary) after each DECA instruction is executed.

HEX ADDRESS	HEX CONTENTS	MNEMONICS/ CONTENTS	COMMENTS
0000	86	LDA	Load accumulator immediate
0001	05	05	with 05.
0002	4A	DECA	
0003	4A	DECA	Repeatedly decrement
0004	4A	DECA	the accumulator.
0005	4A	DECA	
0006	4A	DECA	
0007	4A	DECA	
0008	4A	DECA	
0009	4A	DECA	
000A	4A	DECA	
000B	4A	DECA	
000C	4A	DECA	
000D	4A	DECA	
000E	4A	DECA	
000F	3E	HLT	Halt

Figure 15

This program decrements the contents of
the accumulator from +5 to −8.

3. In step 7, the number in the accumulator changed from 0 to -1. The microprocessor expresses -1 as $\_\_{}_{16}$ or $_____{}_2$. The table you have developed in Figure 16 shows how the microprocessor expresses the signed number from $+5$ to -5 in both hexadecimal and binary. The next program will add signed numbers like these.

AFTER STEP	CONTENTS OF ACCUMULATOR		
	DECIMAL	HEXADECIMAL	BINARY
1	+5	05	0000 0101
2	+4		
3	+3		
4	+2		
5	+1		
6	0		
7	−1		
8	−2		
9	−3		
10	−4		
11	−5	FB	1111 1011

Figure 16

Record results here.

4. Enter the program shown in Figure 17. Use the single step mode to execute the program. What number is in the accumulator after the first instruction is executed? $\_\_{}_{16}$ or $_____{}_2$. What signed decimal number does this represent? _____.

HEX ADDRESS	HEX CONTENTS	MNEMONICS/ CONTENTS	COMMENTS
0000	86	LDA	Load accumulator immediate
0001	05	+5	with +5.
0002	8B	ADD	Add immediate
0003	FB	−5	−5.
0004	8B	ADD	Add immediate
0005	FC	−4	−4
0006	3E	HLT	

Figure 17

Adding signed numbers.

5.   What number is in the accumulator after the second instruction is executed? $\_\_{}_{16}$ or $_____{}_2$. What decimal number does this represent? $_____$.

6.   What number is in the accumulator after the third instruction is executed? $\_\_{}_{16}$ or $_____{}_2$. What signed decimal number does this represent? $_____$.

DISCUSSION

These very simple examples illustrate how the microprocessor represents signed numbers. Further experiments will show that the microprocessor can represent signed numbers between $+127_{10}$ and -128_{10}. You could determine the bit pattern for each negative number by clearing the accumulator and decrementing the required number of times. However, there are much simpler ways of determining the proper bit pattern for negative numbers.

The simplest way is to start with the positive binary equivalent and take the two's complement by changing all 0's to 1's and 1's to 0's and adding 1. The microprocessor has an instruction that will do this for us. It is called the two's complement or Negate instruction. Its mnemonic is NEGA. This instruction changes the number in the accumulator to its two's complement. It is used to change the sign of a number.

PROCEDURE (Continued)

7. Load the program shown in Figure 18. Use the single-step mode to execute the program. Execute the first instruction by depressing the SS key. What number is in the accumulator? $\_\_{}_{16}$ or $_____{}_2$. What signed decimal number does this represent? _____.

8. Execute the second instruction. What number is in the accumulator? $\_\_{}_{16}$ or $_____{}_2$. What signed decimal number does this represent? _____. Compare this with the number in step 7. What affect did the NEGA instruction have? _____
_____.

HEX ADDRESS	HEX CONTENTS	MNEMONICS/ CONTENTS	COMMENTS
0000	86	LDA	Load accumulator immediate
0001	05	+5	with +5.
0002	40	NEGA	Change the number to −5.
0003	40	NEGA	Change it back to +5.
0004	4A	DECA	Decrement the number to +4.
0005	40	NEGA	Change the number to −4.
0006	40	NEGA	Change it back to +4.
0007	3E	HLT	Halt

Figure 18
Using the NEGA instruction.

9. Execute the third instruction. What number is in the accumulator? $\_\_{}_{16}$ or $_____{}_2$. What signed decimal number does this represent? _____. Is your answer the same as that found in step 7? _____.

10. Execute the fourth instruction. This decrements the accumulator so that it now contains the signed decimal number _____.

11. Execute the fifth instruction. What number is in the accumulator? $\_\_{}_{16}$ or $_____{}_2$. What signed decimal number does this represent? _____.

12. Execute the sixth instruction. The number in the accumulator is $\_\_{}_{16}$ once more.

DISCUSSION

The program used the NEGA instruction four times. The first time, the NEGA instruction changed 05_{16} to its two's complement FB_{16}. Referring back to the table you developed in Figure 16, this is the representation for -5_{10}. Thus, the NEGA instruction effectively changes the sign of the number in the accumulator. The next step proved this again by converting -5_{10} back to $+5_{10}$. To further emphasize the point, the number was decremented to $+4_{10}$. The next NEGA instruction changed this to FC_{16} which is the representation for -4_{10}. The final NEGA instruction converts this back to $+4_{10}$. This instruction allows us to convert a positive number to its negative equivalent and vice versa.

In Unit 3, you learned that the MPU can work with signed numbers in the range of $+127_{10}$ to -128_{10} or unsigned numbers in the range of 0 to 255_{10}. This capability results from the way we interpret bit patterns. The following steps will demonstrate this.

PROCEDURE (Continued)

13.   Figure 19 shows a program for adding the unsigned numbers 220_{10} and 27_{10}. Load this program into the Trainer and execute it. The final result in the accumulator is $\_\_{}_{16}$ or $_____{}_{2}$. What unsigned decimal number does this represent? _____.

HEX ADDRESS	HEX CONTENTS	MNEMONICS/ CONTENTS	COMMENTS
0000	86	LDA	Load accumulator immediate
0001	DC	220_{10}	with 220_{10}.
0002	8B	ADD	Add immediate
0003	1B	27_{10}	27_{10}.
0004	3E	HLT	Halt.

Figure 19

Adding unsigned numbers.

14. Figure 20 shows a program for adding the signed numbers -36_{10} and 27_{10}. Load and execute this program. The final result in the accumulator is ___$_{16}$ or _____$_2$. What signed decimal number does this represent? _____.

15. Compare the results obtained in steps 13 and 14. Compare the HEX Contents columns of Figure 19 with that of Figure 20.

HEX ADDRESS	HEX CONTENTS	MNEMONICS/ CONTENTS	COMMENTS
0000	86	LDA	Load accumulator immediate
0001	DC	-36_{10}	with -36_{10}
0002	8B	ADD	Add immediate
0003	1B	$+27_{10}$	$+27_{10}$
0004	3E	HLT	Halt.

Figure 20

Adding signed numbers.

DISCUSSION

This demonstrates that the MPU simply adds bit patterns. It is our interpretation of these patterns that decide whether we are using signed or unsigned numbers. After all, the two programs are identical except for our interpretation of the input and output data.

Negative numbers are often encountered when performing subtract operations. The subtract instruction was shown earlier in Figure 14. Either immediate or direct addressing can be used.

PROCEDURE (Continued)

16. Load the program shown in Figure 21. Execute the program using the single-step mode. What is the number in the accumulator after the first subtract instruction is executed? $\_\_{}_{16}$ or $_____{}_2$ or $\_\_{}_{10}$.

17. What is the number in the accumulator after the second subtract instruction is executed? $\_\_{}_{16}$ or $_____{}_2$. What signed decimal number does this represent? $_____$.

HEX ADDRESS	HEX CONTENTS	MNEMONICS/ CONTENTS	COMMENTS
0000	86	LDA	Load accumulator immediate
0001	2F	47_{10}	with 47_{10}.
0002	80	SUB	Subtract immediate
0003	10	16_{10}	16_{10}
0004	80	SUB	Subtract immediate
0005	23	35_{10}	35_{10}
0006	3E	HLT	Halt

Figure 21
Using the subtract instruction.

DISCUSSION

The first subtract instruction subtracted 16_{10} from 47_{10}, leaving 31_{10}. The second one subtracted 35_{10} from 31_{10}. This produced a result of -4_{10}. However, the MPU expressed -4 in two's complement form (FC_{16} or $1111\ 1100_2$). You will find this to be the case anytime the MPU produces a negative result.

Now let's look at some of the logical instructions available to the microprocessor. The AND and OR instructions are described in Figure 14. Carefully read the description of these instructions given there. While these instructions have many uses, we will demonstrate only one here. Earlier you learned that certain peripheral devices communicate with computers using the ASCII code. Thus, when the "2" key on a teletypewriter is pushed, the computer receives the ASCII code for 2, which is 0011 0010. The ASCII code for 6 is 0011 0110. Notice that the four least significant bits of the ASCII character are the binary value of the corresponding numeral. Thus, we can convert the ASCII characters for the numerals 0 through 9 to binary simply by setting the four most significant bits to 0's. Likewise, we can convert the binary numbers 0000 0000 through 0000 1001 to ASCII by changing the four mos significant bits to 0011.

PROCEDURE (Continued)

18. Load the program shown in Figure 22. Single-step through the first instruction. The number in the accumulator is _ _ _ _ _ _ _ _₂.

19. Execute the second instruction. This AND's the contents of the accumulator with the "mask" _ _ _ _ _ _ _ _. The number in the accumulator after this AND operation is _ _ _ _ _ _ _ _₂. Compare this with the number that was in the accumulator in step 18. Compare both numbers with the mask. A 1 in the original number is retained only if there is a _____ in the corresponding bit position of the mask.

20. Execute the third instruction. In what memory location is the number in the accumulator stored? _____₁₆. What number is now in the accumulator? _ _ _ _ _ _ _ _₂. Does the number still appear in the accumulator after being stored in memory? _____.

HEX ADDRESS	HEX CONTENTS	MNEMONICS/ CONTENTS	COMMENTS
0000	96	LDA	Load the accumulator with
0001	OB	OB	the ASCII character at this address.
0002	84	AND	AND it with
0003	OF	OF	this "mask".
0004	97	STA	Store the binary equivalent
0005	OC	OC	at this address.
0006	8A	ORA	OR the number with
0007	30	30	this "mask".
0008	97	STA	Store the result
0009	OD	OD	here.
000A	3E	HLT	Stop
000B	37	0011 0111	ASCII character for numeral 7.
000C	—	—	Reserved
000D	—	—	Reserved

Figure 22
Using the AND and OR instruction.

21. Execute the fourth instruction. This OR's the contents of the accumulator with the "mask" $\_\,\_\,\_\,\_\,\_\,\_\,\_\,\_{2}$. The number in the accumulator is $\_\,\_\,\_\,\_\,\_\,\_\,\_\,\_{2}$. Compare this with the mask and the number that was in the accumulator in step 20. A 1 is produced in the result whenever there is a _____ in the corresponding bit position of either the original number, the mask, or both.

22. Execute the fifth instruction. This stores the number in memory location _____$_{16}$.

23. Examine memory locations $000B_{16}$, $000C_{16}$, and $000D_{16}$ and compare their contents.

DISCUSSION

The program first converts the ASCII code for the number "7" to the binary number 0000 0111. It does this by ANDing the ASCII code with the "mask" 0000 1111$_{2}$. Notice that a 1 bit in the mask allows the corresponding bit in the original number to be retained. The four most significant bits of the original number are "masked off" because they are ANDed with 0's.

The OR operation restores the ASCII character by attaching 0011 as the four most significant bits.

Experiment 5

Program Branches

OBJECTIVES:

To manipulate the N, Z, V, and C condition code registers and determine the conditions that set and reset these flags.

To verify the operation of a simple multiply by repeated addition program that uses the BEQ conditional branch instruction and the BRA instruction.

To demonstrate the ability to write a program that divides by repeated subtraction and uses a conditional branch and BRA instruction.

To introduce a shorthand method of calculating relative addresses.

To verify the operation of a program that converts BCD numbers to their binary equivalent.

To demonstrate the effect an incorrect relative address can have on a program operation and how the microprocessor trainer can be used to debug programs.

INTRODUCTION

As mentioned previously, conditional branch instructions give the computer the power to make decisions. As the name implies, a certain condition must be met before a branch takes place. The condition code registers monitor the accumulator and signal the presence of a specific condition. If the MPU encounters a conditional branch instruction, it merely checks the condition code registers, or flags, to see if the condition is satisfied. If the specific flag is set, the program branches off to another section. If not, the normal program continues.

Therefore, the conditional branch instructions inherit their power from these simple condition code registers. A sound knowledge of how these flags are set and cleared will enhance your ability as a programmer.

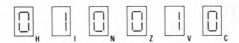

Figure 23
Displaying the conditions of the flags.

Since condition code registers are very important, your Trainer was designed with a special key to allow you to examine these flags. The key is labelled "C" for "Condition Code." When this key is pressed, the state of the condition code registers will be displayed. Each LED displays the contents of one register. The letter just to the right of each LED denotes the corresponding register as shown in Figure 23.

Notice that there are six flag registers. For the moment we aren't concerned with the two left-most flags. They will be covered in a later unit. However, we are interested in the N, Z, V, and C flags, because they indicate conditions that can lead to conditional branches. Notice that the flags can either be set as indicated by a 1 or they can be cleared as indicated by a 0.

In this first portion of the experiment, you will implement a "do-nothing" program that manipulates the condition code registers. Then single-stepping through the program, you will examine how the accumulator changes these flags.

PROCEDURE

1.   Turn on the Trainer and then press the RESET key.

2.   Now, load the program listed in Figure 24 into the Trainer. Once the program is loaded, go back and examine it to insure that it's entered correctly.

      Now look at the first instruction of the program in Figure 24. It has the op code 01 and the mnemonic is "NOP". As the comments column points out, this is a "do-nothing" type of instruction called a "No-Op." In other words, it performs no operation. In this program, the NOP's primary function is to allow you to see the first instruction before it's executed.

HEX ADDRESS	HEX CONTENTS	MNEMONICS/ CONTENTS	COMMENTS
0000	01	NOP	"DO Nothing" Instruction
0001	86	LDA	Load the accumulator immediate
0002	FF	FF_{16}	with FF_{16}.
0003	86	LDA	Load the accumulator immediate
0004	77	77_{16}	with 77_{16}.
0005	86	LDA	Load the accumulator immediate
0006	00	00_{16}	with 00_{16}.
0007	86	LDA	Load the accumulator immediate
0008	01	01_{16}	with 01_{16}.
0009	86	LDA	Load the accumulator immediate
000A	92	92_{16}	with 92_{16}
000B	8B	ADD	Add Immediate
000C	C6	$C6_{16}$	$C6_{16}$
000D	86	LDA	Load the accumulator immediate
000E	08	08_{16}	with 08_{16}.
000F	8B	ADD	Add Immediate
0010	08	08_{16}	08_{16}.
0011	86	LDA	Load the accumulator immediate
0012	01	01_{16}	with 01_{16}.
0013	80	SUB	Subtract immediate
0014	02	02_{16}	02_{16}.
0015	86	LDA	Load the accumulator immediate
0016	77	77_{16}	with 77_{16}.
0017	80	SUB	Subtract immediate
0018	66	66_{16}	66_{16}.
0019	86	LDA	Load the accumulator immediate
001A	49	49_{16}	with 49_{16}.
001B	8B	ADD	Add immediate
001C	60	60_{16}	60_{16}.
001D	86	LDA	Load the accumulator immediate
001E	10	10_{16}	with 10_{16}.
001F	3E	HLT	Halt.

Figure 24

Program to illustrate the condition code
registers.

In previous experiments, you probably noticed that when you single-stepped through programs, you never saw the first instruction. This is because in the "SS" mode, the Trainer executes the first instruction automatically and then stops on the second instruction. This can be somewhat confusing.

To offset this problem, we merely insert the NOP. The Trainer "sees" this as the first instruction, although nothing is accomplished by the NOP. Therefore, the Trainer displays the next instruction, which is the first "real" instruction of the program, permitting you to view it before it's executed.

3. Load the program counter with address 0000 and then press the SS key. Recall that the first four displays represent the address that's currently in the program counter. The two right-most displays show the op code stored at this address. Record the information below.

    PC _ _ _ _ OP CODE _ _

    Now, press the ACCA key and record the contents of the accumulator.

    ACCA _ _

    The contents of the accumulator will be a random number, since we haven't yet executed a program instruction.

    Now, press the CC key and record the contents of the N, Z, V, and C condition code registers below.

    _ _ _ _

    N Z V C

    Again, the states of the flags are random at this time.

4. Now, press the SS key and then the ACCA key. Record the contents of the accumulator below.

    ACCA _ _

    Press key CC and record the state of the N flag below.

    _ _ _ _
    N Z V C

    With the negative number FF$_{16}$ in the accumulator, the negative (N) flag is set.

5. Press the SS key again. The program count should now be 0005_{16} and the op code at this address is 86. Now check and record the contents of the accumulator and the N flag.

ACCA _ _   _ _ _ _

        N Z V C

With the positive number 77_{16} in the accumulator, the N flag is cleared, or reset, to 0.

From the information gathered in steps 4 and 5, what conclusions do you reach with respect to the N flag and the contents of the accumulator?

_____

6. Single-step the program again. The program count is now 0007_{16}. Record the contents of the accumulator and the condition of the Z flag below.

ACCA _ _   _ _ _ _

        N Z V C

With 00_{16} in the accumulator, the Z flag is set.

Press SS and again record the contents of the accumulator and the Z flag below.

ACCA _ _   _ _ _ _

        N Z V C

The accumulator now contains 01_{16} and the Z flag is cleared. What is the relation between the contents of the accumulator and the Z, or zero flag?

_____

7.   Single-step again and record the information below.

ACCA _ _   _ _ = =

              N Z V C

This step loads the number 92_{16} into the accumulator. Bit 7 of the accumulator contains a 1_2 so the N flag is set. Naturally, the Z flag is cleared. The next instruction will add $C6_{16}$ to the contents of the accumulator. As shown below, this operation should generate a carry.

$$
\begin{array}{llll}
1001 & 0010 & = & 92_{16} \\
1100 & 0110 & = & C6_{16} \\
\hline
0101 & 1000 & = & 158_{16}
\end{array}
$$

CARRY —⌐¹

Press the SS key and record the information below.

ACCA _ _   _ _ = _

              N Z V C

The 8-bit accumulator cannot hold the 9-bit sum. However, the carry generated by the addition sets the C flag.

8.   This step loads the number 08_{16} into the accumulator. Press the SS key and record the information below.

ACCA _ _   _ _ = _

              N Z V C

Notice that loading this new number into the accumulator didn't affect the carry (C) flag. The next step will add 08_{16} to the contents of the accumulator (08_{16}).

9.   Press the SS key and record the information below.

ACCA _ _   _ _ = _

              N Z V C

The accumulator now contains the sum of the addition (10_{16}) and the carry flag is cleared.

From the results of steps 8 and 9, you might conclude that the carry flag can be cleared by another _____ _____ that does not result in a carry.

10. Press the SS key. The program count should now be 0013. Record the information below.

ACCA _ _   _ _ - _

          N Z V C

This shows that the accumulator contains 01_{16} and that the N, Z, and C flags are all cleared. When the next instruction is executed, the number 02_{16} will be subtracted from 01_{16} (the contents of the accumulator). As shown below, the subtraction should result in a borrow, setting the C flag.

```
        1
        ↑
Borrow ─┘  0000  0001  =   01₁₆
           0000  0010  =   02₁₆
          ─────────────────────
           1111  1111  =   FF₁₆
```

Notice that the difference is FF_{16}. This will _____ the N flag.
                                        set/clear

11. Press the SS key and record the information below.

ACCA _ _   _ _ - _

          N Z V C

As expected, the difference produced is FF_{16}. Also, the N flag is set, indicating a negative number is in the accumulator and the C flag indicates a borrow occurred.

The next step will execute the instruction that loads 77_{16} into the accumulator. After this LDA operation, the C flag will be _____.
                                                       set/cleared

12. Press the SS key and record the information below.

ACCA _ _   _ _ $\doteq$ _

       N Z V C

Notice that the C flag is still set and that 77_{16} is in the accumulator. Now we will subtract 66_{16} from the accumulator contents (77_{16}).

Press the SS key and record the information below.

ACCA _ _   _ _ $\doteq$ _

       N Z V C

The difference (11_{16}) is now stored in the accumulator and, since no borrow is generated, the C flag is cleared.

13. In this step, the first instruction loads the accumulator with the number 49_{16}. The next instruction adds the number 60_{16} to 49_{16}. As shown below, the addition of these numbers causes an overflow into the sign bit (bit 7) and the sum, $A9_{16}$, appears to be a negative number.

$$
\begin{array}{rcl}
0100\quad 1001 & = & 49_{16} \\
0110\quad 0000 & = & 60_{16} \\
\hline
1010\quad 1001 & = & A9_{16}
\end{array}
$$

Overflow changes ⏋
sign bit.

Of course, this is incorrect and the MPU must be notified of this overflow. This is the purpose of the V flag.

Press the SS key and record the information below.

ACCA _ _   _ _ _ _
              N Z V C

The number 49_{16} is in the accumulator and the N, Z, V, and C flags are cleared.

Single-step once more and then record the information below.

ACCA _ _   _ _ _ _
              N Z V C

The sum $A9_{16}$ is now in the accumulator. Notice that the N **and** V flags are set, indicating that the number in the accumulator is negative and that an overflow occurred.

14.   When the next instruction is executed, the number 10_{16} will be loaded into the accumulator.

Single-step the program and record the information below. Notice that the op code 3E (a halt) is the next instruction, so the program is finished.

ACCA _ _   _ _ _ _
              N Z V C

The accumulator contains the number 10_{16}, and all flags cleared. From this, you might conclude that any instruction that doesn't produce an overflow in the accumulator will _____ the V flag.
                                                    set/clear

DISCUSSION

In this portion of the experiment, you stepped through a simple program that manipulated the condition code registers. In step 4, the negative number FF_{16} was loaded into the accumulator. This set the N flag to 1_2. In step 5, the positive number 77_{16} was loaded into the accumulator. And, as you noted, the N flag was cleared or reset to 0_2. From these two steps you should have concluded that when the number in the accumulator is negative, the N flag is set. And when the accumulator contains a positive number, the N flag is cleared.

In step 6, the accumulator was loaded with 00_{16}. This set the Z flag to 1_2. Next, when 01_{16} was loaded, the Z flag was reset or cleared to 0_2. Your conclusion should have been that when the accumulator contains 00_{16}, the Z flag is set. If it contains any number other than 00_{16}, the Z flag is cleared.

Next, you examined the C flag. When a carry was generated by the addition of the two numbers, 92_{16} and $C6_{16}$, the C flag was set. In step 8, you noted that merely loading a new number into the accumulator did not clear the C flag. The carry flag was cleared by another addition that did not result in a carry. Your conclusion should have been that the C flag can only be cleared by an arithmetic operation that does not result in a carry.

As you proved in steps 10 and 11, a subtraction that results in a borrow also sets the C flag. Again, the C flag was cleared by an arithmetic operation, in this case a subtraction, that did not generate a borrow. Therefore, the C flag can only be cleared or reset to 0_2 by an arithmetic operation that does not result in a borrow or carry.

You concluded this phase of the experiment by adding two positive numbers, the sum of which overflowed into the sign bit of the accumulator. This set the V or overflow flag, showing that the sum should not be a negative number as the N flag indicated. The next LDA instruction cleared the V flag. From this, you should conclude that the V flag is cleared by any instruction that doesn't produce an overflow.

In the next sections of this experiment, you will step through a few branching programs that illustrate the use of the branch always (BRA) instruction and certain conditional branch instructions. These branch instructions were discussed in Unit 4, and you will verify their operation. We'll begin with the multiply by repeated addition program.

PROCEDURE (Continued)

15. Enter the program listed in Figure 25 into the Trainer. This program multiplies 05_{16} and 02_{16} and stores the product in address 0013_{16}. Recheck the program to insure that it's entered correctly.

16. This is the same program that you stepped through in Unit 4. Notice that the program contains two branch instructions; the BEQ (Branch if Equal Zero) at address 0005_{16} and the BRA (Branch Always) at address $000E_{16}$.

    The branch if equal zero (BEQ) instruction implies by its name that a conditional branch will occur when the _____ flag is set.

HEX ADDRESS	HEX CONTENTS	MNEMONICS/ CONTENTS	COMMENTS
0000	4F	CLRA	Clear the accumulator.
0001	97	STA	Store the product
0002	13	13	in location 13_{16}.
0003	96	LDA	Load the accumulator with the
0004	12	12	multiplier from location 12_{16}.
0005	27	BEQ	If the multiplier is equal to zero,
0006	09	09	branch down to the Halt instruction.
0007	4A	DECA	Otherwise, decrement the multiplier.
0008	97	STA	Store the new value of the
0009	12	12	multiplier back in location 12_{16}.
000A	96	LDA	Load the accumulator with the
000B	13	13	product from location 13_{16}.
000C	9B	ADD	Add
000D	11	11	the multiplicand to the product.
000E	20	BRA	Branch back to instruction
000F	F1	F1	in location 01.
0010	3E	HLT	Halt.
0011	05	05	Multiplicand.
0012	02	02	Multiplier.
0013	—	—	Product.

Figure 25
Program to multiply by repeated addition.

17. Now, set the program counter to 0000 and single-step through the program, recording the information in the chart of Figure 26. Notice that you will be monitoring the Z flag. A comments column is provided so you can make notes about each step. Use the program listing as a reference for each op code and the corresponding operand.

18. When the BEQ instruction is executed and the Z flag is set, the program branches to the _____ instruction.

   When the multiplier was 02_{16}, the program halted on the _____ pass through the program.

   If the multiplier is changed to 06_{16}, how many passes would the program make before it halts? _____.

19. Examine the contents of address 0013_{16} and record below.

   0013 _ _.

STEP	PROGRAM COUNTER	OPCODE	ACCA	Z FLAG	COMMENTS
1 2 3					
4 5 6					
7 8 9					
10 11 12					
13 14 15					
16 17 18					
19 20					

Figure 26
Single-stepping through the Multiply by
repeated addition program.

DISCUSSION

The chart that you completed should be similar to the one shown in Figure 27. Compare the charts.

The first step we don't see, since it's executed before the Trainer stops at address 0001. Nevertheless, we do see the result of this clear accumulator instruction because the accumulator contains 00. When step 1 is executed, 00_{16} is stored in location 0013_{16}. Step 2 brings us to address 0003_{16} which loads the accumulator with the multiplier, in this example, 02_{16}. The BEQ instruction is next, but the Z flag is cleared so the program continues on the normal route. Next the multiplier is decremented to 01_{16} and then stored in location 0012_{16}. Now the product (00_{16}) is loaded and the multiplicand (05_{16}) is added directly. This produces the new product, 05_{16}. Now the program encounters the BRA, or branch always instruction and it branches back to address 0001_{16}.

Here the new product is stored away and the multiplier is loaded again. It's 01_{16} this time, so the program continues on through the BEQ instruction, the multiplier is decremented to 00_{16}, and the multiplicand 05_{16} is added to the product. The new product ($0A_{16}$) is still in the accumulator. Once again, the BRA instruction loops flow back to address 0001_{16} and the product is stored in address 0013_{16}.

The multiplier is now loaded and, since it's been decremented to 00_{16}, it sets the Z flag. The BEQ instruction checks the Z flag, finds that it's set and branches to the halt instruction at address 0010_{16}. Therefore, the program makes two complete passes, before the multiplier becomes 00_{16}. On the third pass through, BEQ terminates the program because the Z flag is set.

The multiplier sets the count and determines how many additions will be performed. If the multiplier is changed to 06_{16}, the program will make six complete loops, halting on the seventh loop. The BEQ will only be satisfied when the multiplier has been reduced to 00.

All branch instructions use relative addressing. In Unit 4, we discussed the method used to calculate the destination address for a branch instruction. However, another shorthand type procedure that's quite popular with programmers can be used. With this technique, you simply count in hexadecimal. For a forward branch, you begin at 00_{16} and count up to the destination address.

STEP	PROGRAM COUNTER	OPCODE	ACCA	Z FLAG	COMMENTS
1	0001	97	00	1	Store the product (00_{16}) in address 0013_{16}.
2	0003	96	00	1	Load the accumulator with the multiplier (02_{16}) from address 0012_{16}.
3	0005	27	02 ↑ Multiplier	0	BEQ. Check the Z flag. It's not set so continue.
4	0007	4A	02	0	Decrement the multiplier (02_{16}).
5	0008	97	01 ↑ New Multiplier	0	Store the new multiplier (01_{16}) at address 0012_{16}.
6	000A	96	01	0	Load the accumulator with the product (00) at address 0013_{16}.
7	000C	9B	00	1	Add the multiplicand (05) giving new product.
8	000E	20	05 ↑ New Product	0	Branch back to address 0001_{16}.
9	0001	97	05	0	Store the product (05_{16}) in address 0013_{16}.
10	0003	96	05	0	Load the accumulator with the multiplier (01_{16}) located at address 0012_{16}.
11	0005	27	01	0	BEQ. Check Z flag. It's not set so continue.
12	0007	4A	01	0	Decrement the multiplier (01_{16}).
13	0008	97	00 ↑ New Multiplier	1	Store the new Multiplier (00_{16}) at address 0012_{16}.
14	000A	96	00	1	Load the accumulator with the product (05_{16}) at address 0013_{16}.
15	000C	9B	05	0	Add the multiplicand (05_{16}) giving new product.
16	000E	20	OA ↑ New Product	0	Branch back to address 0001_{16}.
17	0001	97	OA	0	Store the product (OA_{16}) in address 0013_{16}.
18	0003	96	OA	0	Load the accumulator with the multiplier (00_{16}) from address 0012_{16}.
19	0005	27	00	1	BEQ. Check the Z flag. Now it's set. Branch to address 0010_{16}.
20	0010	3E	00	1	Halt.

Figure 27

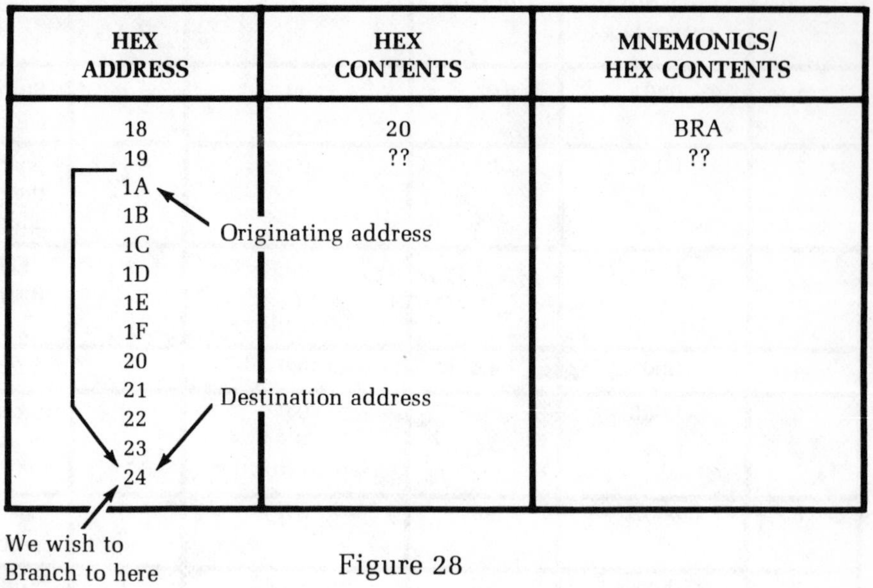

HEX ADDRESS	HEX CONTENTS	MNEMONICS/ HEX CONTENTS
18	20	BRA
19	??	??
1A		
1B		
1C	*Originating address*	
1D		
1E		
1F		
20		
21	*Destination address*	
22		
23		
24		

We wish to
Branch to here

Figure 28

For example, in the program of Figure 28, we want to branch from address 18_{16} to address 24_{16}. Recall that the relative address is added to the contents of the program counter. After the BRA instruction and its operand (the relative address) have been fetched, the program counter is pointing to address $1A_{16}$. Therefore, we begin our count at address $1A_{16}$. Then we count forward in hex as shown in Figure 29. When we reach the destination address, the hexadecimal count is the relative address. In this case, it's $0A_{16}$, and we insert this operand at address 19_{16}.

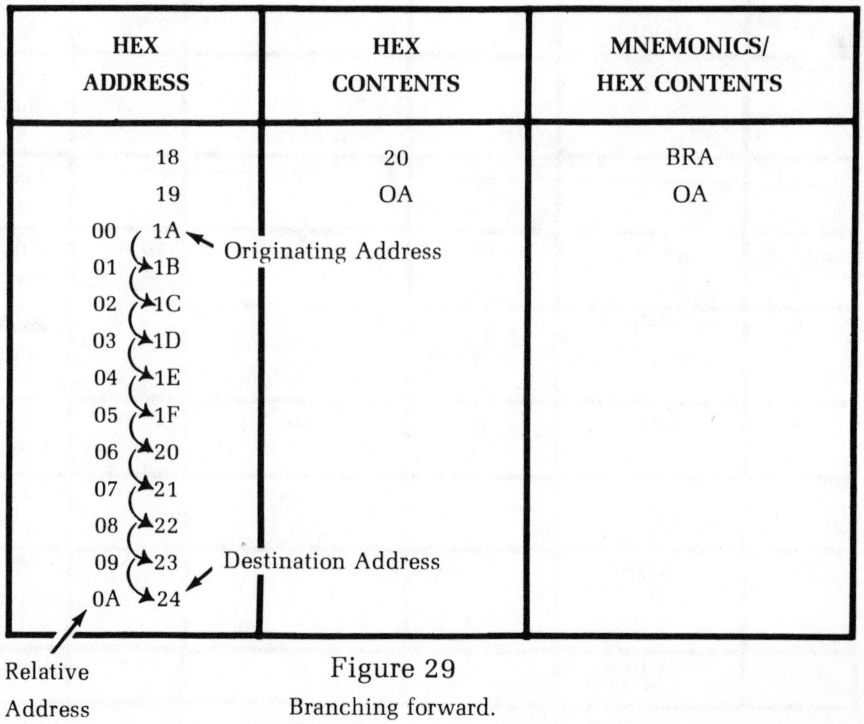

HEX ADDRESS	HEX CONTENTS	MNEMONICS/ HEX CONTENTS
18	20	BRA
19	OA	OA
00 1A	*Originating Address*	
01 1B		
02 1C		
03 1D		
04 1E		
05 1F		
06 20		
07 21		
08 22		
09 23	*Destination Address*	
0A 24		

Relative
Address

Figure 29

Branching forward.

To branch backward in the program, we simply count down using negative hex numbers. It may sound more difficult, but once you are accustomed to it, you will find it easier to use than the previous method you learned.

For example, in the program shown in Figure 30A, we wish to branch back to address 58_{16}. The BRA instruction, at address $5D_{16}$ is fetched and the program count points to address $5F_{16}$. Figure 30B shows how we calculate the address for this backward branch. We begin with FF_{16}, and count down. When we reach the destination address (58_{16}), the count at that point is the relative address, in this case $F9_{16}$.

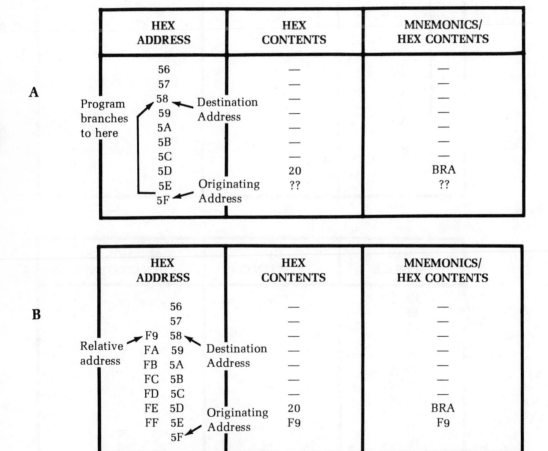

Figure 30
Branching back.

Figure 31 shows another example of computing the relative address for a larger branch. The branch instruction is at address $B0_{16}$ and therefore, the origination address is $B2_{16}$. We calculate the relative address as shown in Figure 31B. Starting with FF_{16} at address $B1_{16}$, we count down to the destination address $A0_{16}$. As the count indicates, the relative address to get to $A0_{16}$ is EE_{16}.

	HEX ADDRESS		HEX CONTENTS	MNEMONICS/ HEX CONTENTS
We wish to branch to here	A0	Destination Address	—	—
	A1		—	—
	A2		—	—
	A3		—	—
	A4		—	—
	A5		—	—
	A6		—	—
	A7		—	—
	A8		—	—
	A9		—	—
	AA		—	—
	AB		—	—
	AC		—	—
	AD		—	—
	AE		—	—
	AF		—	—
	B0		26	BNE
	B1	Originating Address	??	??
	B2			

A

Figure 31

	HEX ADDRESS		HEX CONTENTS	MNEMONICS/ HEX CONTENTS
Relative Address	EE	A0	—	—
	EF	A1	—	—
	F0	A2	—	—
	F1	A3	—	—
	F2	A4	—	—
	F3	A5	—	—
	F4	A6	—	—
	F5	A7	—	—
	F6	A8	—	—
	F7	A9	—	—
	F8	AA	—	—
	F9	AB	—	—
	FA	AC	—	—
	FB	AD	—	—
	FC	AE	—	—
	FD	AF	—	—
	FE	B0	26	BNE
	FF	B1	EE	EE
		B2		

B

In the next section of this experiment, you will write a program that will divide by repeated subtraction. You will probably have two branches in this program; a forward branch and a branch back. Use this new technique to calculate the relative addresses for both branches.

PROCEDURE (Continued)

20. In Unit 4, we discussed a program that divides by repeated subtraction. The flow chart for this program is shown in Figure 32. Using this flow chart as a guide and the instructions presented in Figure 33, write a program that divides by repeated subtraction.

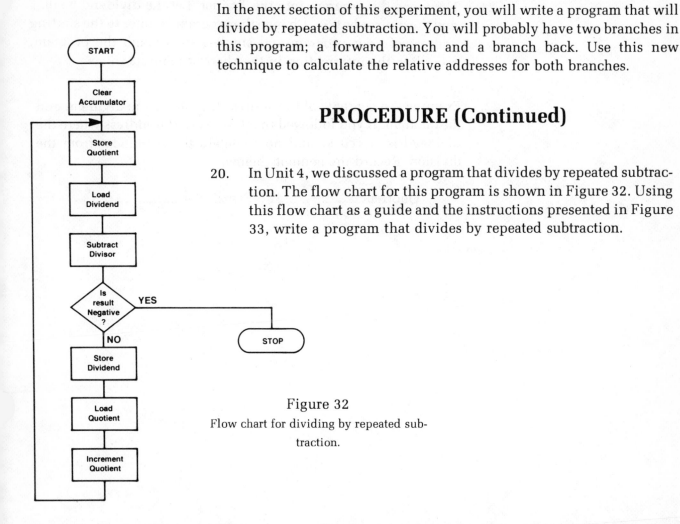

Figure 32

Flow chart for dividing by repeated subtraction.

INSTRUCTION	MNEMONIC	ADDRESSING MODE			
		IMMEDIATE	DIRECT	RELATIVE	INHERENT
Load Accumulator	LDA	86	96		
Clear Accumulator	CLRA				4F
Decrement Accumulator	DECA				4A
Increment Accumulator	INCA				4C
Store Accumulator	STA		97		
Add	ADD	8B	9B		
Subtract	SUB	80	90		
Branch Always	BRA			20	
Branch if Carry Set	BCS			25	
Branch if Equal Zero	BEQ			27	
Branch if Minus	BMI			2B	
Halt	HLT				3E

Figure 33

Instructions to be used.

21. Now load the program into the Trainer. Let the dividend be $0B_{16}$ and the divisor be 05_{16}. Change the program counter to the starting address of your program and single-step through the program, recording the information in the chart of Figure 34.

22. Examine the contents of the address that stores the dividend and the quotient. If you followed the flow chart, the address where the dividend is stored should now contain the remainder from the division. Record the contents below.

Quotient _____ _____   Remainder _____ _____

STEP	PROGRAM COUNTER	OPCODE	ACCA	N FLAG.	COMMENTS

Figure 34

DISCUSSION (Continued)

Now you've written a program that incorporates an unconditional branch and a conditional branch. Hopefully, you calculated the relative addresses using the shorthand technique just discussed. Our program for the divide by repeated subtraction is listed in Figure 35. If you followed the flow chart, your program should be similar to this.

HEX ADDRESS	HEX CONTENTS	MNEMONIC/HEX CONTENTS	COMMENTS
0000	4F	CLRA	Clear the accumulator.
0001	97	STA	Store in the quotient which
0002	13	13	is at address location 13$_{16}$.
0003	96	LDA	Load the accumulator with the
0004	11	11	dividend from location 11$_{16}$.
0005	90	SUB	Subtract the
0006	12	12	divisor from the dividend.
0007	2B	BMI	If the difference is negative,
0008	07	07	branch down to the Halt instruction.
0009	97	STA	Otherwise, store the difference
000A	11	11	back in location 11$_{16}$.
000B	96	LDA	Load the accumulator with the
000C	13	13	quotient.
000D	4C	INCA	Increment the quotient by one.
000E	20	BRA	Branch back to instruction
000F	F1	F1	in location 01.
0010	3E	HLT	Halt.
0011	OB	OB	Dividend (11$_{16}$).
0012	05	05	Divisor (5$_{16}$).
0013	—	—	Quotient.

Figure 35

Dividing by repeated subtraction.

Notice that we used the BMI (Branch if Minus) conditional branch instruction. Therefore, the N or negative flag will satisfy the branch when it's set. Figure 36 charts our program as we single-stepped through it. Since the program subtracts the divisor from the dividend and stores the difference as the new dividend, at the conclusion of the program the dividend is actually the remainder of the division. When $0B_{16}$ is divided by 05_{16}, the quotient should be 02_{16} and the remainder 01_{16}.

STEP	PROGRAM COUNTER	OPCODE	ACCA	N FLAG	COMMENTS
1	0001	97	00	0	Store the quotient (00_{16}) at address 0013_{16}.
2	0003	96	00	0	Load the accumulator with the dividend from address 0011_{16}.
3	0005	90	OB ↑ Dividend	0	Subtract the divisor (05_{16}) at address 0012_{16} from the accumulator.
4	0007	2B	06 ↑ After subtraction	0	BMI. Check the N flag. It's not set so continue.
5	0009	97	06	0	Store the difference (06_{16}) back in address 0011_{16}.
6	000B	96	06	0	Load the accumulator with the quotient (00_{16}) at address 0013_{16}.
7	000D	4C	00	0	Increment the quotient.
8	000E	20	01 ↑ Quotient after INC	0	Branch back to the instruction at address 0001_{16}.
9	0001	97	01	0	Store the quotient (01_{16}) at address 0013_{16}.
10	0003	96	01	0	Load the accumulator with the dividend (06_{16}) at address 0011_{16}.
11	0005	90	06 ↑ Dividend Now	0	Subtract the divisor (05_{16}) at address 0012_{16} from the accumulator.
12	0007	2B	01 ↑ After Subtraction	0	BMI. Check the N flag. It's not set so continue.
13	0009	97	01	0	Store the difference (01_{16}) back in address 0011_{16}.
14	000B	96	01	0	Load the accumulator with the quotient (01_{16}) at address 0013_{16}.
15	000D	4C	01	0	Increment the quotient.
16	000E	20	02 ↑ Quotient after INC.	0	Branch back to the instruction at address 0001_{16}.
17	0001	97	02	0	Store the quotient (02_{16}) at address 0013_{16}.
18	0002	96	02	0	Load the accumulator with the dividend (01_{16}) at address 0011_{16}.
19	0005	90	01	0	Subtract the divisor (05_{16}) at address 0012_{16} from the accumulator.
20	0007	2B	FC ↑ Negative Number	1	BMI. Check the N flag. Now it's set so branch to the instruction at address 0010_{16}.
21	0010	3E	FC	1	Halt.

Figure 36

So far, we've used the conditional branch instructions only to exit a loop and then halt program execution. However, these branch instructions become even more powerful when they are used to "chain" together different portions of a program. Figure 37 shows an example of this chaining effect. The program starts and runs through the first loop until the conditional branch BEQ is satisfied. Then it exits this loop and starts another. When the BEQ condition is satisfied in the second loop, another exit is performed, and another portion of the program is executed.

A strategically placed conditional branch at the end of the program can cause a branch back to the beginning that will repeat the program again and again. In the next portion of this experiment, you will load the BCD-to-binary conversion program that you studied earlier. Then you will step through the program and watch as the Trainer executes each instruction.

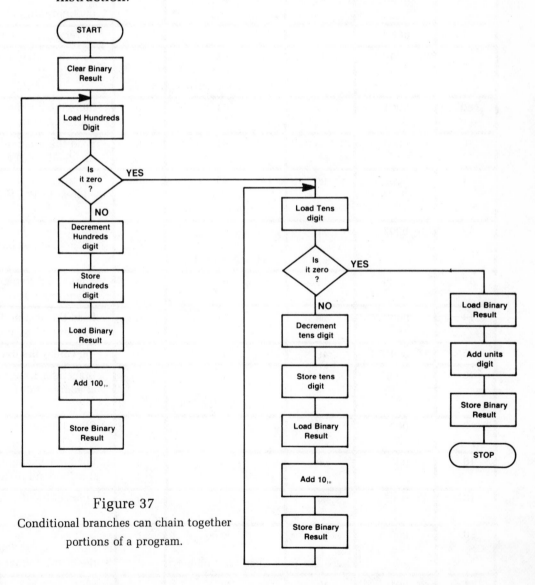

Figure 37
Conditional branches can chain together
portions of a program.

PROCEDURE (Continued)

23. Load the program listed in Figure 38 into the Trainer. The BCD number 117_{10} will be converted to binary by this program.

HEX ADDRESS	HEX CONTENTS	MNEMONICS/ CONTENTS	COMMENTS
0000	4F	CLRA	Clear the Accumulator.
0001	97	STA	Store 00
0002	2B	2B	in location 2B. This clears the binary result.
0003	96	LDA	Load direct into the accumulator
0004	28	28	the hundreds BCD digit.
0005	27	BEQ	If the hundreds digit is zero, branch
0006	0B	0B	forward to the instruction in location 12_{16}.
0007	4A	DECA	Otherwise, decrement the accumulator.
0008	97	STA	Store the result as the new
0009	28	28	hundreds BCD digit.
000A	96	LDA	Load direct into the accumulator
000B	2B	2B	the binary result.
000C	8B	ADD	Add immediate
000D	64	64	100_{10} to the binary result.
000E	97	STA	Store away the new
000F	2B	2B	binary result.
0010	20	BRA	Branch
0011	F1	F1	back to the instruction in location 03_{16}.
0012	96	LDA	Load direct into the accumulator
0013	29	29	the tens BCD digit.
0014	27	BEQ	If the tens BCD digit is zero, branch
0015	0B	0B	forward to the instruction in location 21_{16}.
0016	4A	DECA	Otherwise, decrement the accumulator.
0017	97	STA	Store the result as the new
0018	29	29	tens BCD digit.
0019	96	LDA	Load direct into the accumulator
001A	2B	2B	the binary result.
001B	8B	ADD	Add immediate
001C	0A	0A	10_{10} to the binary result.
001D	97	STA	Store away the new
001E	2B	2B	binary result.
001F	20	BRA	Branch
0020	F1	F1	back to the instruction in location 12_{16}.
0021	96	LDA	Load direct into the accumulator
0022	2B	2B	the binary result.
0023	9B	ADD	Add direct
0024	2A	2A	the units BCD digit.
0025	97	STA	Store away the new
0026	2B	2B	binary result.
0027	3E	HLT	Halt.
0028	01	01	Hundreds BCD digit.
0029	01	01	Tens BCD digit.
002A	07	07	Units BCD digit.
002B	—	—	Reserved for the binary result.

Figure 38

Program for converting BCD to binary.

The BEQ instruction is used for the conditional branches in this program. This means that MPU will monitor the _____ flag to determine if the condition is set.

24. Now set the program counter to 0000 and single-step through the program recording the information in the chart of Figure 39. Notice that, at strategic steps, you should stop and answer questions before you continue.

25. What is the hundreds BCD digit at this time? _____ The result is now 64_{16}, which is _____ in the decimal number system.

   Now return to the Trainer and continue stepping through the program.

26. What is the tens BCD digit at this time? _____.

   The result is now $6E_{16}$. This is the equivalent of _____ in the decimal number system.

   Now return to the Trainer and step through the remainder of the program.

27. Examine address $002B_{16}$ and record the result below.

   _____$_{16}$

   Convert this number to its decimal equivalent.

   $75_{16} =$ _____$_{10}$

STEP	PROGRAM COUNTER	OPCODE	ACCA	Z FLAG	COMMENTS
1					
2					
3					
4					
5					
6					
7					
8					
Stop! Return to Step 25.					
9					
10					
11					
12					
13					
14					
15					
16					
17					
18					
Stop! Return to step 26.					
19					
20					
21					
22					
23					
24					
25					

Figure 39

DISCUSSION

Now you've verified the operation of the BCD-to-binary conversion program. The chart that you completed should match the one shown in Figure 40.

Since the BEQ instruction is used for the conditional branches in the program, we monitored the Z flag. In this example, the BCD number 117_{10} was converted to its binary equivalent 75_{16}. This program will convert BCD numbers as high as 255_{10}, to their binary equivalent.

The program isn't as complicated as it might appear. The hundreds and tens BCD digits are used to set a count. Each pass through a loop decrements the BCD digit, or count, and then adds the equivalent hexadecimal positional value for that BCD digit. For example, in the hundreds conversion loop, 64_{16} is added to the binary result for each hundreds BCD digit. Hence, the BCD digit sets the count. Then the count is decremented by one and the program loops back and runs through again. When the count is zero, that BCD digit has been added the correct number of times and the program branches off to another loop. This continues until the program halts.

Stepping through the program, you found that after Step 8, the Trainer had completed one loop through the hundreds BCD portion of the program. The count was 00_{16} and the binary result was 64_{16}, or the binary equivalent of 100_{10}. On the next pass through, the program branches to the tens BCD loop.

The first loop through, the tens BCD portion of the program was completed at step 18. The binary result was $6E_{16}$, which is the equivalent of 110_{10}. The tens BCD digit had been decremented to 00_{16}. Then all that remained was to add the units BCD digit (07_{10}) and the conversion process was complete.

You verified the final result by checking the binary result at location $002B_{16}$. Here you found the hex number 75_{16}. When you converted this number to its decimal equivalent, you found that 75_{16} equals 117_{10}. Also, if you converted 75_{16} to binary, you would find the number $0111\ 0101_2$; which is the (binary) equivalent of 117_{10}, so the program works.

The most frequent mistake made by programmers when using the branch instructions is the improper computation of the relative address. An improperly coded relative address not only prevents the program from executing properly, but can even wipe out portions of the program. In the next section of this experiment, you will witness the result of an incorrect relative address and the effect it has on the program. In this example, we will use the binary-to-BCD conversion program you studied earlier.

STEP	PROGRAM COUNTER	OPCODE	ACCA		Z FLAG	COMMENTS
1	0001	97		00	1	Store 00 in address 002B$_{16}$. This clears the binary result.
2	0003	96		00	1	Load the accumulator with the Hundreds BCD digit (01$_{16}$).
3	0005	27	Hundreds BCD→ Digit	01	0	BEQ. Check the Z flag. It's clear so continue.
4	0007	4A		01	0	Decrement the BCD Hundreds Digit.
5	0008	97	New→ Hundreds Digit	00	1	Store the new Hundreds Digit (00).
6	000A	96		00	1	Load the accumulator with the Binary Result (00$_{16}$).
7	000C	8B		00	1	Add to the binary result 64$_{16}$.
8	000E	97	Binary→ Result Now	64	0	Store away the new binary result.
9	0010	20		64	0	Branch back to address 0003$_{16}$.
10	0003	96		64	0	Load the accumulator with the Hundreds BCD digit (00).
11	0005	27		00	1	BEQ. Check the Z flag. It's set so branch to address 0012$_{16}$.
12	0012	96		00	1	Load the accumulator with the tens BCD digit (01$_{16}$).
13	0014	27	Tens BCD→ Digit	01	0	BEQ. Check the Z flag. It's clear so continue.
14	0016	4A		01	0	Decrement the tens BCD digit (01$_{16}$).
15	0017	97	New Tens→ Digit	00	1	Store the new tens BCD digit.
16	0019	96		00	1	Load the accumulator with the binary result (64$_{16}$).
17	001B	8B		64	0	Add OA$_{16}$ to the binary result.
18	001D	97	New Binary→ Result	6E	0	Store away the new binary result.
19	001F	20		6E	0	Branch back to address 0012$_{16}$.
20	0012	96		6E	0	Load the accumulator with the tens BCD digit (00).
21	0014	27		00	1	BEQ. Check the Z flag. It's set so branch to address 0021$_{16}$.
22	0021	96		00	1	Load the accumulator with the binary result (6E$_{16}$).
23	0023	9B		6E	0	Add the units BCD digit (07$_{16}$).
24	0025	97	New Binary→ Result	75	0	Store the new binary result (75$_{16}$).
25	0027	3E		75	0	Halt.

Figure 40

Single-stepping through the BCD-to-
binary conversion program.

HEX ADDRESS	HEX CONTENTS	MNEMONICS/ CONTENTS	COMMENTS
0000	4F	CLRA	Clear the accumulator.
0001	97	STA	Store 00
0002	2B	2B	in location $002B_{16}$. This clears the hundreds digit.
0003	97	STA	Store 00.
0004	2C	2C	in location $002C_{16}$. This clears the tens digit.
0005	97	STA	Store 00.
0006	2D	2D	in location $002D_{16}$. This clears the units digit.
0007	96	LDA	Load direct into the accumulator
0008	2A	2A	the binary number to be converted.
0009	80	SUB	Subtract immediate
000A	64	64	100_{16}.
000B	25	BCS	If a borrow occurred, branch
000C	0A	0A	forward to the instruction in location 0016_{16}.
000D	97	STA	Otherwise, store the result of the subtraction
000E	2A	2A	as the new binary number.
000F	96	LDA	Load direct into the accumulator
0010	2B	2B	the hundreds digit of the BCD result.
0011	4C	INCA	Increment the hundreds digit.
0012	97	STA	Store the hundreds digit
0013	2B	2B	back where it came from.
0014	20	BRA	Branch
0015	F1	F1	back to the instruction at address 0007_{16}.
0016	96	LDA	Load direct into the accumulator
0017	2A	2A	the binary number.
0018	80	SUB	Subtract immediate
0019	0A	0A	10_{16}.
001A	25	BCS	If a borrow occurred, branch
001B	09	09	forward to the instruction in location 0025_{16}.
001C	97	STA	Otherwise, store the result of the subtraction
001D	2A	2A	as the new binary number.
001E	96	LDA	Load direct into the accumulator
001F	2C	2C	the tens digit.
0020	4C	INCA	Increment the tens digit.
0021	97	STA	Store the tens digit.
0022	2C	2C	back where it came from.
0023	20	BRA	Branch
0024	F1	F1	back to the instruction at address 0016_{16}.
0025	96	LDA	Load direct into the accumulator
0026	2A	2A	the binary number.
0027	97	STA	Store it in
0028	2D	2D	the units digit.
0029	3E	HLT	Halt.
002A	75	75	Place binary number to be converted at this address.
002B	—	—	Hundreds digit
002C	—	—	Tens digit } Reserved for BCD result.
002D	—	—	Units digit

Figure 41

A program with an incorrect relative address.

PROCEDURE (Continued)

28. Load the program listed in Figure 41 into the Trainer. This program should convert the binary number $0111\ 0101_2$ (75_{16}) into its BCD equivalent. However, one of the relative addresses is **incorrect**. Part of this exercise is to locate the incorrect relative address and correct it.

29. Now set the program counter to 0000 and single-step through the program. Record the results in the chart of Figure 42. Notice that we're monitoring the carry (C) flag because the program uses the BCS (Branch if Carry Set) instruction.

STEP	PROGRAM COUNTER	OPCODE	ACCA	C FLAG	COMMENTS
1					
2					
3					
4					
5					
6					
7					
8					
9					
10					
11					
12					
13					
14					
15					
16					
17					
18					
19					
20					

Figure 42
Single-Stepping through the binary-to-
BCD conversion program.

30. Examine addresses $002B_{16}$, $002C_{16}$, and $002D_{16}$; record the results below.

002B __ __ Hundreds BCD Digit

002C __ __ Tens BCD Digit

002D __ __ Units BCD Digit

Obviously, there is something wrong with the program. Although the hundreds and tens digits are believable, the units digit of 11 is impossible. Remember, a decimal number can only have a units digit of from 0 to 9_{10}.

31. Use the program listing and the chart that you've compiled and locate the error in the program. Then record the address of the instruction below.

HINT: The problem is with the relative address for one of the branch instructions. When one of these addresses is incorrect, the program branches to the wrong address, possibly skipping portions of the program. Therefore, first determine the portions of the program that produced the wrong result and work back until you find the problem.

Address __ __ __ __   Incorrect Relative Address __ __

32. Now calculate the correct relative address (operand) and record it below.

Correct Relative Address __ __.

DISCUSSION

This exercise should have demonstrated the versatility of your Trainer to assist you in "debugging" programs. When you examined addresses $002B_{16}$, $002C_{16}$, and $002D_{16}$, you found these results.

002B	0	1	Hundreds BCD Digit
002C	0	0	Tens BCD Digit
002D	1	1	Units BCD Digit

Obviously, the units BCD digit is incorrect. Since the units digit is wrong, we begin to debug at this portion of the program. This happens to be the least complex section of the program because the binary number is simply loaded into the accumulator and stored in address $002D_{16}$. Comparing the chart that you compiled against the program listing, we find that this portion of the program seems to be executing correctly.

Therefore, we move back to the tens BCD digit portion of the program. Checking the program listing, we find that the tens BCD portion of the program begins at address 0016_{16}. But as the chart in Figure 43 shows, when the program is single-stepped the tens BCD digit loop actually starts at address 0017_{16}. This is the wrong address. We find the problem when we move back to step 14 of the chart. This is the BCS (Branch if Carry Set) instruction at address $000B_{16}$. However, instead of branching to address 0016_{16} as the comments column suggests, the program goes to address 0017_{16}. Therefore, the relative address at address $000C_{16}$ must be incorrect. When we check this relative address, we find that it should be 09_{16}, instead of $0A_{16}$.

But, how did this incorrect operand affect the program? Following the chart in Figure 43, we find that the hundreds BCD portion of the program worked correctly. On the second loop through this portion of the program, the subtraction resulted in a borrow and the C flag was set. Hence, the BCD instruction produced the desired branch.

But, instead of branching to address 0016_{16}, where we would have found a load accumulator instruction (96_{16}) with an operand of $2A_{16}$, the program branches to address 0017_{16}. The Trainer now interprets the operand ($2A_{16}$) as an instruction or op code. The op code 2A, as you may recall, represents a valid instruction which is "Branch if Plus." The MPU checks the N flag and finds it set, because at this time, the negative number AD_{16} is in the accumulator. Therefore, the condition is not satisfied, and the Trainer continues on to the next instruction.

Single-stepping again (now we are at step 16) the next op code is 0A. Actually, this should be the operand for the subtract instruction at address 0018_{16}. But since we are off by one, it appears to be the op code. The Trainer checks the op code 0A and finds that it's an inherent instruction to "clear the overflow flag." It executes this instruction.

Step 17 finds the program at address $001A_{16}$. Here, we encounter another BCS conditional branch instruction. The C flag is still set so we branch to address 0025_{16}. The program works properly from this point on.

Therefore, this one incorrect relative address caused the program to skip the tens BCD portion of the program. The tens unit was never subtracted, so it carried over into the units BCD digit. This produced the wrong units digit of 11_{10}.

STEP	PROGRAM COUNTER	OPCODE	ACCA	C FLAG	COMMENTS
1	0001	97	00	0	Store 00 in Hundreds Digit.
2	0003	97	00	0	Store 00 in tens Digit.
3	0005	97	00	0	Store 00 in units Digit.
4	0007	96	00	0	Load the accumulator with the Binary number (75_{16}).
5	0009	80	75	0	Subtract 64_{16} from accumulator
6	000B	25	11	0	BCS. Check C flag for borrow. It's clear so continue.
7	000D	97	11	0	Store away the new binary number.
8	000F	96	11	0	Load the accumulator with the Hundreds Digit (00).
9	0011	4C	00	0	Increment the Hundreds Digit.
10	0012	97	01	0	Store the Hundreds Digit.
11	0014	20	01	0	Branch back to address 0007_{16}.
12	0007	96	01	0	Load the accumulator with the Binary Number (11_{16}).
13	0009	80	11	0	Subtract 64_{16} from accumulator. BCS. Check C Flag for borrow.
14	000B	25	AD	1	It's set so branch to address 0016_{16}.
15	[Tens BCD] ← Wrong Address 0017 2A		AD	1	What's this?
16	0019	OA	AD	1	
17	001A	25	AD	1	BCS. Check C Flag. It's still set so branch to address 0025_{16}.
18	[Units BCD] 0025	96	AD	1	Load the accumulator with the Binary number.
19	0027	97	11	1	Store it in the units Digit.
20	0029	3E	11	1	Halt.

Figure 43

Locating the incorrect relative address.

PROCEDURE (Continued)

33. Now change the operand at address $000C_{16}$ from $0A_{16}$ to 09_{16}.

34. Also change the number at address $002A_{16}$ to 75_{16}. This is the number that the program will convert to its BCD equivalent.

35. Reset the program counter to 0000 and single-step through the program comparing the program listing with the results that you obtain.

36. Examine the addresses listed below and record the information stored there.

      002B __ __   Hundreds BCD Digit

      002C __ __   Tens BCD Digit

      002D __ __   Units BCD Digit

Is this the correct BCD representation for the number 75_{16}? _____.

DISCUSSION

When the program is corrected by inserting the relative address (09_{16}) at address $000C_{16}$, we find that it works perfectly. After single-stepping through the program, we examine the BCD digits stored at addresses $002B_{16}$, $002C_{16}$, and $002D_{16}$. The hundreds digit is 01_{10}, the tens digit is 01_{10}, and the units digit is 07_{10}. Therefore, the BCD equivalent of the binary number $0111\ 0101_2$ (75_{16}) is 117_{10}.

Experiment 6

Additional Instructions

OBJECTIVES:

To verify the operation of the ADC instruction when used in a multiple-precision addition program.

To investigate the hazard of using the ADC instruction when a carry is not desired.

To demonstrate your ability to write a multiple-precision subtraction program using the SBC instruction.

To demonstrate your ability to write a routine that will multiply any 4-bit binary number times 16_{10} using the ASLA instruction.

To verify the operation of a BCD packing program that uses the ASLA instruction.

To verify the operation of the DAA instruction when used in a BCD multiple-precision addition program.

INTRODUCTION

One of the measures of a microprocessor's power is the size of the instruction set. In other words, more instructions generally mean more potential power. You saw the economy that resulted with the addition of branch instructions in the previous experiment. In this experiment, we will examine four additional instructions; the ADC or add with carry, the SBC or subtract with carry, the ASLA or arithmetic shift accumulator left, and the DAA or decimal adjust accumulator.

The discussion in Unit 4 explained the purpose of each instruction. In this experiment, we will restrict our activity to verifying that each instruction works as explained.

In the previous experiment, you examined the condition code registers and how the MPU monitors these flag registers to initiate conditional branches. Yet, these condition code registers are also monitored for other instructions. For example, the ADC (add with carry) and SBC (subtract with carry) instructions key on the C or carry flag. If an ADC instruction is executed and the carry flag is set, one is added to the least significant bit in the accumulator. Likewise, if the C flag is set when an SBC instruction is executed, one is subtracted from the least-significant bit of the accumulator. Remember, the C flag represents a "borrow" to the subtract instruction.

In the first portion of this experiment, we will verify the operation of the ADC instruction with a program for multiple precision arithmetic. Then we will examine one of the hazards of using this instruction.

PROCEDURE

1. Turn on the Trainer and press the RESET key.

2. Load the program listed in Figure 44 into the Trainer. This program performs multiple-precision addition of two 16_{10} bit numbers. The augend $1B93_{16}$ will be added to the addend $C0EA_{16}$ by this program. Of course, the program can add any numbers that are 16_{10} bits or less.

HEX ADDRESS	HEX CONTENTS	MNEMONICS/ CONTENTS	COMMENTS
0000	01	NOP	No operation
0001	96	LDA	Load the accumulator direct with the
0002	OE	OE	least significant byte of the addend.
0003	9B	ADD	Add direct the
0004	10	10	least significant byte of the augend.
0005	97	STA	Store the result in the
0006	12	12	least significant byte of the sum.
0007	96	LDA	Load the accumulator direct with the
0008	OF	OF	most significant byte of the addend.
0009	99	ADC	Add with carry direct the
000A	11	11	most significant byte of the augend.
000B	97	STA	Store the result in the
000C	13	13	most significant byte of the sum.
000D	3E	HLT	Halt
000E	EA	EA	Least significant byte ⎫
000F	CO	CO	Most significant byte ⎬ addend
0010	93	93	Least significant byte ⎫
0011	1B	1B	Most significant byte ⎬ augend
0012	—	—	Least significant byte ⎫
0013	—	—	Most significant byte ⎬ sum

Figure 44
Program for multiple-precision addition.

3. Change the program counter to 0000 and single-step through the program, recording the information in the chart of Figure 45. Notice that we are monitoring the carry (C) flag.

STEP	PROGRAM COUNTER	OPCODE	ACCA	C FLAG	COMMENTS
1					
2					
3					
4					
5					
6					
7					

Figure 45

4. Examine memory location 0012_{16} and 0013_{16} and record the sum below.

SUM _ _ _ _

5. Add the binary numbers below. These numbers are the binary equivalent of the two hex numbers added by the program just executed.

		MSB		LSB	
$COEA_{16}$	=	1100	0000	1110	1010
$1B93_{16}$	=	0001	1011	1001	0011
SUM	=				

Now, convert the binary sum to its hexadecimal equivalent and record below.

SUM _ _ _ _

Does this match the sum obtained in step 4? _____

6.   Now load the program of Figure 46 into the Trainer. This program simply adds two binary numbers and produces a carry. Hence, it will set the C flag. You will see its purpose in a moment.

Execute the program by pressing the DO key and then entering address 0000.

7.   Examine the carry (C) condition code register. The C flag is _____.

 set/reset

HEX ADDRESS	HEX CONTENTS	MNEMONICS/ CONTENTS	COMMENTS
0000	86	LDA	Load the accumulator immediate
0001	EA	EA	with EA_{16}.
0002	8B	ADD	Add immediate
0003	93	93	93
0004	3E	HLT	Halt

Figure 46
Program adds two numbers and produces carry.

8. Enter the program listed in Figure 47 into the Trainer. Notice that this is the same multiple-precision addition program previously executed, with the exception that the ADD Instruction has been replaced by the ADC instruction, as shown by the shaded section.

HEX ADDRESS	HEX CONTENTS	MNEMONICS/ CONTENTS	COMMENTS
0000	01	NOP	No operation
0001	96	LDA	Load the accumulator direct with the
0002	OE	OE	least significant byte of the addend
0003	99	ADC	Add with carry direct the
0004	10	10	least significant byte of the augend.
0005	97	STA	Store the result in the
0006	12	12	least significant byte of the sum.
0007	96	LDA	Load the accumulator direct with the
0008	OF	OF	most significant byte of the addend.
0009	99	ADC	Add with carry direct the
000A	11	11	most significant byte of the augend.
000B	97	STA	Store the result in the
000C	13	13	most significant byte of the sum.
000D	3E	HLT	Halt
000E	EA	EA	Least significant byte ⎫ addend
000F	CO	CO	Most significant byte ⎭
0010	93	93	Least significant byte ⎫ augend
0011	1B	1B	Most significant byte ⎭
0012	—	—	Least significant byte ⎫ sum
0013	—	—	Most significant byte ⎭

Figure 47

Multiple-precision addition program with instruction at address 003_{16} changed.

9. Set the program counter to 000 and single-step through the program, recording the information in the chart of Figure 48.

10. Examine memory locations 0012_{16} and 0013_{16}. Record the sum below.

SUM _ _ _ _

Compare this sum to the previous sum recorded in step 4. Are they the same? _____.
       yes/no

Why are the sums different? _____

_____

_____

From this demonstration, what conclusion can you draw concerning the use of the ADC instruction? _____

_____

_____

STEP	PROGRAM COUNTER	OPCODE	ACCA	C FLAG	COMMENTS
1					
2					
3					
4					
5					
6					
7					

Figure 48

DISCUSSION

In steps 1 through 3 of this experiment, you loaded a multiple-precision addition program similar to the one you studied in Unit 4. Single-stepping through the program, you witnessed the operation of the ADC instruction. The chart you complied should be similar to the chart in Figure 49. When you checked memory locations 0012_{16} and 0013_{16}, you found the LSB and MSB respectively of the 16_{10}-bit sum. The sum should have been $DC7D_{16}$.

In step 5 you added the binary equivalents of the hex numbers, $COEA_{16}$ and $1B93_{16}$. The sum was the binary equivalent of the sum produced by the program, as shown below.

		MSB		LSB	
			1		
$COEA_{16}$	=	1100	0000	1110	1010
$1B93_{16}$	=	0001	1011	1001	0011
SUM	=	1101	1100	0111	1101

As you noticed, a carry is generated by the addition of the least significant bytes of the two numbers. When you were single-stepping through the program, you observed this carry because the C flag was set. The addition of the most significant bytes did not produce a carry. Therefore, the carry flag was cleared.

STEP	PROGRAM COUNTER	OPCODE	ACCA	C FLAG	COMMENTS
1	0001	96	Random	Random	Load the accumulator with the LSB of Addend (EA_{16}).
2	0003	9B	EA	Random	Add the LSB of the Augend (93_{16}).
3	0005	97	7D	1	Store result in LSB of sum.
4	0007	96	7D	1	Load the accumulator with the MSB of the Addend (CO_{16}).
5	0009	99	CO	1	Add with carry the MSB of the Augend ($1B_{16}$).
6	000B	97	DC	0	Store result in MSB of Sum.
7	000D	3E	DC	0	Halt.

Figure 49

When you converted the binary number to hexadecimal, you found that
the sum was the same as that produced by the program.

$$1101 \quad 1100 \qquad 0111 \quad 1101$$

$$D \qquad C \qquad 7 \qquad D$$

In step 6, you loaded a simple program that added the numbers EA_{16} and
93_{16}. Of course, the addition generated a carry, as you witnessed when
you checked the C flag and found it set.

In step 8, you loaded another multiple-precision addition program into
the Trainer. The only difference between this program and the previous
multiple-precision addition program was that the first add instruction
was the ADC (add with carry), rather than the ADD. Then you single-
stepped through the program and completed the chart of Figure 48. Your
chart should be similar to the one shown in Figure 50.

STEP	PROGRAM COUNTER	OPCODE	ACCA	C FLAG	COMMENTS
1	0001	96	Random	1	Load the accumulator with the LSB of Addend (EA_{16}).
2	0003	99	EA	1	Add with carry the LSB of the Augend 93_{16}).
3	0005	97	7E	1	Store result in LSB of sum. Load the accumulator with the MSB
4	0007	96	7E	1	of Addend (CO_{16}).
5	0009	99	CO	1	Add with carry the MSB of the Augend ($1B_{16}$).
6	000B	97	DC	0	Store result in MSB of sum.
7	000D	3E	DC	0	Halt.

Figure 50
Single-stepping through the multiple-
precision addition program where both
add instructions are ADC.

When you examined the sum at addresses 0012_{16} and 0013_{16}, you found $DC7E_{16}$. The correct sum, as you verified earlier, should have been $DC7D_{16}$. If you checked the chart compiled while single-stepping through the program, the reason for this incorrect answer should have been evident. The carry flag was set even before the program was executed. Therefore, when the Trainer executed the first ADC instruction, it automatically added the carry (1_2) to the sum of the least significant bytes. Hence, the result 7E was one greater than the correct sum of 7D.

From this demonstration you should have reached the conclusion that the ADC instruction should not be used unless you are positive of the condition of the C flag. You must remember that the C flag is only reset by an arithmetic operation that doesn't produce a **carry** or a **borrow**. For example, in the program that worked properly, we used the simple ADD instruction for the first addition. Naturally, this instruction ignores the condition of the C flag, so it doesn't matter if it's set or reset. This is a simple way of playing it safe. The second addition used the ADC instruction because we wanted any carry from the least significant byte to be reflected in the most significant byte.

The SBC (subtract with carry) instruction is similar to the ADC instruction because it also monitors the C flag to indicate a borrow. In the next section of this experiment, you will write a program that uses the SBC instruction for multiple-precision subtraction of 16_{10}-bit numbers.

PROCEDURE (Continued)

11. Write a program that will perfrom multiple-precision subtraction of two 16_{10}-bit (2-byte) numbers. The following guidelines define the problem.

    a. The program must subtract a 16_{10}-bit subtrahend from a 16_{10}-bit minuend and store the difference in memory.

    b. Use the direct addressing mode.

    c. Select the op codes from the instruction listing in Figure 51.

12. Now load the program. Enter 9721_{16} in the locations reserved for the minuend and 7581_{16} in the locations reserved for the subtrahend.

13. Single-step through the program and observe its operation. Examine the locations where the difference is stored and record the 2-byte difference below.

    DIFFERENCE _____ _____ _____ _____

INSTRUCTION	MNEMONIC	ADDRESSING MODE			
		IMMEDIATE	DIRECT	RELATIVE	INHERENT
Load Accumulator	LDA	86	96		
Clear Accumulator	CLRA				4F
Decrement Accumulator	DECA				4A
Increment Accumulator	INCA				4C
Store Accumulator	STA		97		
Add	ADD	8B	9B		
Subtract	SUB	80	90		
Add with Carry	ADC	89	99		
Subtract with Carry	SBC	82	92		
Arithmetic Shift Accumulator Left	ASLA				48
Decimal Adjust Accumulator	DAA				19
Halt	HLT				3E

Figure 51
Instructions.

DISCUSSION

If you made a flow chart of the problem, your flow chart probably looks like the one shown in Figure 52. Your program should be similar to the solution shown in Figure 53. After stepping through the program on the Trainer, the difference of the subtraction should have been $21A0_{16}$. If you didn't obtain this answer, go back and recheck your program.

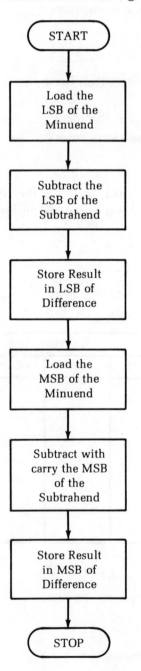

Figure 52
Flow chart for multiple-precision sub-traction.

HEX ADDRESS	HEX CONTENTS	MNEMONICS/ CONTENTS	COMMENTS
0000	96	LDA	Load accumulator direct with
0001	0D	0D	least significant byte of minuend
0002	90	SUB	Subtract direct
0003	0F	0F	least significant byte of subtrahend
0004	97	STA	Store result in
0005	11	11	least significant byte of difference
0006	96	LDA	Load accumulator direct with
0007	0E	0E	most significant byte of minuend
0008	92	SBC	Subtract with carry
0009	10	10	most significant byte of the subtrahend
000A	97	STA	Store result in
000B	12	12	most significant byte of difference
000C	3E	HLT	Halt
000D	21	21	Least significant byte $\}$ Minuend
000E	97	97	Most significant byte
000F	81	81	Least significant byte $\}$ Subtrahend
0010	75	75	Most significant byte
0011	—	—	Least significant byte $\}$ Difference
0012	—	—	Most significant byte

Figure 53

Program for multiple-precision subtraction.

You may have used the SBC instruction for the first subtraction. If you did, this might explain the problem, because if the C flag is set when this instruction is executed a 1 will be borrowed from the difference. Therefore, your answer would have been 1 less than the correct answer, or $219F_{16}$. If the carry flag was cleared before you executed the program, the result would still be correct.

In the next section of this experiment, we will examine the ASLA (arithmetic shift accumulator left) instruction. You will also write a simple program that uses this instruction to multiply any 4_{10}-bit number by 16_{10}. This simple routine will prove it's usefulness later.

Recall from the discussion in Unit 4 that each ASLA operation multiplies the contents of the accumulator by two.

PROCEDURE (Continued)

14. Use the instructions listed in Figure 51 and write a program that uses the ASLA instruction to multiply any 4_{10}-bit number by 16_{10}.

15. Enter your program into the Trainer and then have your program multiply OF_{16} (15_{10}) by 16_{10}. Record the product below.

    $OF_{16} \times 16_{10} =$ _____ $_{16}$.

16. Convert the product obtained to its decimal equivalent.

    Decimal equivalent _____ $_{10}$.

    Now check your result by multiplying 15_{10} times 16_{10}.

    $15_{10} \times 16_{10} =$ _____ $_{10}$.

17. In this program, the multiplier is determined by the number of ASLA instructions. How many ASLA instructions are required to produce a multiplier of 4_{10}? _____.

DISCUSSION

The program for this simple routine is shown in Figure 54. Notice that is uses 4_{10} ASLA instructions to produce the required multiplier of 16_{10}. If your program worked properly, the final product should have been $F0_{16}$. Converting this number to its decimal equivalent, we find that $F0_{16}$ equals 240_{10}. When we multiplied 15_{10} times 16_{10}, we also found the product was 240_{10}. Therefore, the program works.

Only two ASLA instructions are necessary to produce a multiplier of 4_{10}; three ASLA instructions will result in a multiplier of 8_{10}.

Another use for the ASLA instruction is to pack two BCD digits into a single byte. This "packing" can result in a significant savings of memory if many BCD numbers are used. Let's verify the operation of the BCD packing program that was presented in Unit 4.

HEX ADDRESS	HEX CONTENTS	MNEMONICS/ CONTENTS	COMMENTS
0000	96	LDA	Load the accumulator with the
0001	09	09	4-bit multiplicand
0002	48	ASLA	Shift the accumulator
0003	48	ASLA	four places to the left
0004	48	ASLA	multiplying the multiplicand by
0005	48	ASLA	16_{10}.
0006	97	STA	Store the product
0007	0A	0A	at this location
0008	3E	HLT	Halt
0009	0F	0F	4-bit multiplicand
000A	—	—	Product

Figure 54

Program that uses the ASLA instruction
to multiply a 4-bit number times 16_{10}.

PROCEDURE (Continued)

18. Enter the BCD packing program listed in Figure 55 into the Trainer. The unpacked BCD numbers are 09_{10} and 03_{10}.

HEX ADDRESS	OPCODES/ CONTENTS	MNEMONICS/ CONTENTS	COMMENTS
0000	01	NOP	Do nothing
0001	96	LDA	Load into the accumulator direct
0002	0D	0D	the unpacked most significant BCD digit.
0003	48	ASLA	Shift it four places
0004	48	ASLA	to the left.
0005	48	ASLA	
0006	48	ASLA	
0007	9B	ADD	Add the
0008	0E	0E	unpacked least significant BCD digit.
0009	97	STA	Store the result
000A	0C	0C	in the packed BCD number
000B	3E	HLT	Halt
000C	00	00	Packed BCD number
000D	09	09	Unpacked most significant BCD digit.
000E	03	03	Unpacked least significant BCD digit.

Figure 55
Program to pack two BCD digits into a single byte.

19. Set the program counter to 0000 and single-step through the program, recording the information below. Where it is indicated, convert the hexadecimal contents of the accumulator to the binary equivalent.

Program Count	Op code	ACCA	Binary Equivalent
0001	96	Random	Random
0003	48	____	____
0004	48	____	____
0005	48	____	____
0006	48	____	____
0007	9B	____	____
0009	97	____	____
000B	3E	HALT	

20. Examine the packed BCD number at address $000C_{16}$ and record it below.

Packed BCD Number _____

DISCUSSION

As you can see, the BCD packing program is very simple. Nevertheless, simple routines such as this can be combined in many programs, easing the task of programming. Most programmers either commit these general purpose routines to memory or file them away for future reference.

The results you obtained by stepping through the program should be similar to those shown below.

PROGRAM COUNT	OP CODE	ACCA	BINARY EQUIVALENT
0001	96	Random	Random
0003	48	09	0000 1001
0004	48	12	0001 0010 After 1st shift
0005	48	24	0010 0100 After 2nd shift
0006	48	48	0100 1000 After 3rd shift
0007	9B	90	1001 0000 After 4th shift
0009	97	93	1001 0011
000B	3E		

As the listing shows, the most significant BCD digit (09_{10}) is loaded into the accumulator. Four ASLA shifts take place, moving this digit progressively to the left. Following these four shifts, the most significant BCD digit is properly positioned. Now the program simply adds the least significant BCD (03_{10}) to the contents of the accumulator and then stores the sum. Checking the address of the packed BCD number, we find 93_{10}.

When BCD numbers are added, we encounter yet another problem. Often, the sum is the correct BCD number. But, just as frequently, it isn't. In Unit 4, the reason for this inconsistency was discussed. However, your Trainer has an instruction, called the "Decimal Adjust Accumulator" (DAA), that can correct the sum of BCD numbers, producing the desired result.

In the next portion of this experiment, we will demonstrate the need for the DAA instruction by first adding two BCD numbers without using the DAA instruction. Then we will check the sum. Next, we will correct the program by inserting DAA instructions and again examine the BCD sum.

PROCEDURE (Continued)

21. Load the program listed in Figure 56 into your Trainer. This program adds the BCD numbers 3792_{10} and 5482_{10}, storing the sum in address 0011_{16} and 0012_{16}.

22. RESET the Trainer and execute the program by first pressing the DO key and entering address 0000.

23. Again, press the RESET key and then examine the sum stored at address 0011_{16} and 0012_{16}. The most significant byte of the sum is at address 0011_{16} and the least significant byte is at address 0012_{16}. Record the sum below.

SUM _____

Is this the correct BCD sum for the addition of the numbers 3792_{10} and 5482_{10}? _____.

yes/no

HEX ADDRESS	HEX CONTENTS	MNEMONICS/ CONTENTS	COMMENTS
0000	96	LDA	Load the accumulator direct with
0001	0E	0E	the least significant byte of addend.
0002	9B	ADD	Add direct
0003	10	10	the least significant byte of augend
0004	97	STA	Store the result in
0005	12	12	the least significant byte of BCD sum.
0006	96	LDA	Load the accumulator direct with
0007	0D	0D	the most significant byte of addend
0008	99	ADC	Add with carry
0009	0F	0F	the most significant byte of augend
000A	97	STA	Store the result in
000B	11	11	the most significant byte of BCD sum.
000C	3E	HLT	Halt
000D	37	37	Most significant byte ⎫ BCD Addend
000E	92	92	Least significant byte ⎭
000F	54	54	Most significant byte ⎫ BCD Augend
0010	82	82	Least significant byte ⎭
0011	—		Most significant byte ⎫ BCD Sum
0012	—		Least significant byte ⎭

Figure 56

Incorrect program for multiple-precision
addition of BCD numbers.

24. Now load the corrected multiple-precision BCD addition program listed in Figure 57 into your Trainer. Notice that the only changes between this program and the previous program are the additions of the NOP instructions and the two DAA instructions following the addition operations.

25. Change the program counter to 0000 and single-step through the program, recording the information below.

STEP 1 _____ _____

           PROGRAM COUNT   OP CODE

STEP 2 _____ _____ _____

           PROGRAM COUNT   OP CODE   ACCA

STEP 3 _____ _____ _____ _____

           PROGRAM COUNT   OP CODE   ACCA   C FLAG

HEX ADDRESS	HEX CONTENTS	MNEMONICS/ CONTENTS	COMMENTS
0000	01	NOP	Do nothing
0001	96	LDA	Load the accumulator direct with the
0002	11	11	least significant byte of addend.
0003	9B	ADD	Add direct
0004	13	13	the least significant byte of augend.
0005	19	DAA	Decimal adjust the sum to BCD.
0006	97	STA	Store the result in the
0007	15	15	least significant byte of BCD sum
0008	96	LDA	Load the accumulator direct with the
0009	10	10	most significant byte of addend.
000A	99	ADC	Add with carry the
000B	12	12	most significant byte of augend.
000C	19	DAA	Decimal adjust the sum to BCD.
000D	97	STA	Store the result in the
000E	14	14	most significant byte of BCD sum.
000F	3E	HLT	Halt.
0010	37	37	Most significant byte } BCD Addend
0011	92	92	Least significant byte }
0012	54	54	Most significant byte } BCD Augend
0013	82	82	Least significant byte }
0014	—	—	Most significant byte } BCD Sum
0015	—	—	Least significant byte }

Figure 57
Program for adding multiple-precision
BCD numbers.

The sum of the addition of the least significant bytes is now in the accumulator. Is this the correct BCD sum for the numbers 92_{10} and 82_{10}? _____

yes/no

When the DAA instruction (op code 19) is executed, will this number be corrected? _____.

yes/no

STEP 4   _____   _____   _____   _____

PROGRAM COUNT   OP CODE   ACCA   C FLAG

As you can see, the DAA instruction did correct the left-most digit by adding 60_{16} to the sum. Since the result 14_{10} appears to be a legitimate BCD number, how did the MPU know it was not the valid BCD sum? _____

_____

STEP 5   _____   _____   _____   _____

PROGRAM COUNT   OP CODE   ACCA   C FLAG

STEP 6   _____   _____   _____   _____

PROGRAM COUNT   OP CODE   ACCA   C FLAG

STEP 7   _____   _____   _____   _____

PROGRAM COUNT   OP CODE   ACCA   C FLAG

It's obvious that this number ($8C_{16}$) is not the BCD sum of 37_{10} and 54_{10}. What number will the MPU add to $8C_{16}$ to produce the desired BCD sum? _____.

STEP 8   _____   _____   _____   _____

PROGRAM COUNT   OP CODE   ACCA   C FLAG

STEP 9   _____   _____   _____

PROGRAM COUNT   OP CODE   ACCA

26.   Now examine the BCD sum at addresses 0014_{16} and 0015_{16} and record below.

SUM _____$_{10}$.

DISCUSSION

When you executed the first program to add BCD numbers, it was obvious that the sum 8C14 was not the correct BCD number. The answer should have been 9274_{10}. Naturally, the MPU considered these BCD numbers as hexadecimal numbers, hence, the hexadecimal sum.

However, when the program was modified by the addition of DAA (decimal adjust accumulator) instructions after each addition operation, the result was the correct BCD number. As you stepped through the program you saw the DAA instruction in operation.

At step 3, the BCD numbers 92_{10} and 82_{10} had been added and the accumulator was supposedly storing the sum 14_{10}. A carry was generated by the setting of the C flag. However, the sum was not correct. Instead of 14_{10}, the sum should have been 174_{10}. To the MPU, the addition looked something like this.

$$
\begin{array}{llll}
 & 1001 & 0010_2 & = 92_{16} \\
\text{C FLAG} \quad 1000 & 0010_2 & = 82_{16} \\
\hline
1 \quad \text{Carry} \quad 0001 & 0100_2 & 114_{16}
\end{array}
$$

If we ignore the carry, the sum 14_{16} appears to be a legitimate BCD number. Nevertheless, the sum would be incorrect. Taking the carry flag into consideration, remember it's just an extension of the accumulator, we find the sum is 114_{16}. In hex, this is the correct sum of the two numbers.

In step 4, the DAA instruction had been executed and, as you witnessed, the number 14_{16} had been adjusted to the correct BCD sum of 74_{10}. The carry flag was set, indicating that the sum of the two left-most 4-bit binary numbers was larger than 1001_2 (9_{16}). Actually, it was $1\ 0001_2$. When the DAA instruction was executed, the MPU followed the conversion rules and adjusted the sum by adding 60_{16} as shown below.

Carry					Carry	
1	0001	0100_2	=		1	14_{16}
	0110	0000_2	=			60_{16}
1	0111	0100_2	=		1	74_{16}

The result is 74_{16} with a carry of 1_{16}. This is the correct BCD sum for the two BCD numbers. If we include the carry, the result is 174_{10} which is indeed the decimal sum of 92_{10} and 82_{10}. However, this exceeds the capacity of our storage locations, since they're only 8-bits long, so the carry is carried forward to the addition of the most significant bytes of the numbers in the next step.

As you continued single-stepping through the program, the most significant bytes were loaded and added with the ADC instruction. At step 7, the sum of this addition was in the accumulator. It was obvious that the sum $8C_{16}$ wasn't a BCD number. To adjust this number to the correct BCD sum, 06_{16} was added by the DAA instruction. The BCD adjusted sum 92_{10} was the result.

In the final step of the experiment, you verified program operation by examining the BCD sum at locations 0014_{16} and 0015_{16}. Here you should have found the sum 9274_{10}.

Experiment 7

New Addressing Modes

OBJECTIVES:

To demonstrate the extended addressing mode.

To demonstrate the indexed addressing mode.

To gain experience using the instruction set and registers of the MPU.

NOTE 1:   If the Trainer you are using has a Model number ET-3400A, it will not be necessary for you to add the two RAM IC's (listed under "Material Required") to your Trainer. After reading the Introduction, begin this experiment at Procedure step 6.

NOTE 2:   If the Trainer you are using has a Model number ET-3400, check IC locations IC16 and IC17. If these two locations do not contain IC's (2112 Heath number 443-721), begin this experiment at Procedure step 1. If these two locations are equipped with the 2112 IC's, begin this experiment at Procedure step 6.

MATERIAL REQUIRED

1 — Microprocessor Trainer

2 — 2112-2 IC's (Heath Number 443-721)

INTRODUCTION

In Unit 5, you learned that the MPU has two new addressing modes called extended and indexed addressing. Either of these addressing modes can be used to reach operands anywhere in memory. By contrast, the direct addressing mode can be used only when the operand is in the first 256_{10} bytes of memory.

PROCEDURE

1. Turn your ET-3400 Microprocessor Trainer off and unplug it.

2. Locate the two 2112-2 IC's (Heath number 443-721) that were supplied with the EB-6401-30 Parts Pack. Notice that these IC's are packed in conductive foam.

NOTE: These IC's are rugged, reliable components. However, normal static electricity discharged from your body through an IC pin to an object can damage the IC. Install these IC's without interruption as follows:

    A. Remove the IC from its package with both hands.

    B. Hold the IC with one hand and straighten any bent pins with the other hand.

    C. Refer to Figure 58. Position the pin 1 end of the IC over the index mark on the circuit board.

    D. Be sure each IC pin is properly started into the socket. Then push the IC down.

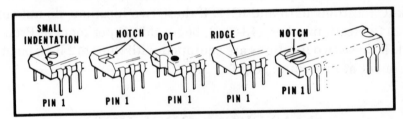

Figure 58

3. Install one of the IC's in the empty socket labelled IC16 on the ET-3400 Trainer.

4. Install the other IC in the socket labelled IC17.

NOTE: Until now, you could not use the extended addressing mode because the ET-3400 Trainer had only 256_{10} bytes of RAM memory. The installation of the two RAM IC's in the above steps has added an additional 256_{10} bytes of RAM memory necessary for the extended addressing mode.

5. Plug in your Trainer and turn it on.

6. Using the AUTO mode, load the numbers 00 through 0F into memory locations 0100 through 010F, respectively.

7. Using the EXAM and FWD keys, verify that the above numbers were stored in those addresses.

DISCUSSION

The ET-3400A Trainer required no hardware modification to acquire 512_{10} bytes of RAM in addresses 0000_{16} through $01FF_{16}$. The two 2114 RAM IC's at IC14 and IC15 already have this capacity. However, the ET-3400 Trainer uses 2112 RAM IC's. The two IC's at IC14 and IC15 contain only the first 256_{10} bytes of memory from 0000_{16} to $00FF_{16}$. Therefore, to extend the RAM capacity of the ET-3400 trainer an additional 256_{10} bytes, it may have been necessary to install two additional 2112 IC's at locations IC16 and IC17. The starting address of this new RAM is 0100_{16} and extends through $01FF_{16}$ for a total of 512_{10} bytes. When operands are placed at addresses above $00FF_{16}$, the extended addressing mode is generally used.

PROCEDURE (Continued)

8. Figure 59 shows a program for adding a list of numbers. Because the numbers are in addresses higher than $00FF_{16}$, the extended addressing mode is used. Load this program into the Trainer and verify that you have loaded it properly.

9. Execute the program using the single-step mode. The first instruction sets the contents of accumulator A to _____.

10. Examine the program counter and accumulator A after each instruction is executed. Each time an ADDA extended instruction is executed, the program counter is advanced _____ bytes.

11. Examine the contents of accumulator A after the final instruction is executed. The number in accumulator A is _____.

12. Refer to your instruction set summary card. How many MPU cycles are required to execute this program? _____.

DISCUSSION

The program adds the ten numbers giving the sum 55_{10} or 37_{16}. It requires 51 MPU cycles. Notice that the program itself takes up 32_{10} bytes of memory. The data (the ten numbers) use another 10_{10} bytes.

A repetitive program like this one is an excellent candidate for indexed addressing. Let's see how the same job can be done using indexed addressing.

HEX ADDRESS	HEX CONTENTS	MNEMONICS/ CONTENTS	COMMENTS
0100	4F	CLRA	Clear accumulator A
0101	BB	ADDA	Add the first number
0102	01	01	which is at this
0103	20	20	address.
0104	BB	ADDA	Add the second number.
0105	01	01	
0106	21	21	
0107	BB	ADDA	Add the third number.
0108	01	01	
0109	22	22	
010A	BB	ADDA	
010B	01	01	
010C	23	23	
010D	BB	ADDA	
010E	01	01	
010F	24	24	
0110	BB	ADDA	
0111	01	01	
0112	25	25	
0113	BB	ADDA	Continue until all numbers are
0114	01	01	added.
0115	26	26	
0116	BB	ADDA	
0117	01	01	
0118	27	27	
0119	BB	ADDA	
011A	01	01	
011B	28	28	
011C	BB	ADDA	
011D	01	01	
011E	29	29	
011F	3E	WAI	Stop.
0120	01	01	First number.
0121	02	02	Second number.
0122	03	03	Third number.
0123	04	04	
0124	05	05	•
0125	06	06	•
0126	07	07	•
0127	08	08	
0128	09	09	
0129	0A	0A	Tenth number.

Figure 59

Adding a list of numbers using extended
addressing.

PROCEDURE (Continued)

13. Figure 60 shows a program for adding the same list of numbers. However it uses indexed addressing. Load this program into the Trainer and verify that you have loaded it correctly.

HEX ADDRESSES	HEX CONTENTS	MNEMONICS/ CONTENTS	COMMENTS
0130	4F	CLRA	Clear accumulator A
0131	CE	LDX#	Load the index register immediately
0132	01	01	with the address of
0133	20	20	the first number in the list.
0134	AB	ADDA, X	Add to accumulator A indexed
0135	00	00	with 00 offset.
0136	08	INX	Increment index register.
0137	8C	CPX#	Compare the index register immediately
0138	01	01	with one greater than the address
0139	2A	2A	of the last number in the list.
013A	26	BNE	If there is no match
013B	F8	F8	branch back to here.
013C	3E	WAI	Otherwise, halt.

Figure 60

Adding the list of numbers using indexed
addressing.

14. Execute the program using the single-step mode. After each step, record the contents of the program counter, accumulator A, and the index register in Figure 61.

15. Compare the programs of Figures 59 and 60. Which requires fewer instructions?

16. Refer to the instruction set summary card. How many machine cycles are required to execute the program shown in Figure 59 _____? Compare this with the number of machine cycles required for the program in Figure 60.

STEP NUMBER	CONTENTS AFTER EACH STEP		
	PC	ACCA	INDEX
1			
2			
3			
4			
5			
6			
7			
8			
9			
10			
11			
12			
13			
14			
15			
16			
17			
18			
19			
20			
21			
22			
23			
24			
25			
26			
27			
28			
29			
30			
31			
32			
33			
34			
35			
36			
37			
38			
39			
40			
41			
42			
43			

Figure 61
Record values here.

DISCUSSION

This example illustrates that when a repetitive task is to be done, indexed addressing can save many bytes of memory. In many cases, indexed addressing requires more MPU cycles and therefore, a longer time to execute. Generally, time is of little importance compared to saving a substantial number of memory bytes.

Let's look at some other ways that indexed addressing is used.

PROCEDURE (Continued)

17. Write a program that will clear memory locations 0120_{16} through $01A0_{16}$. It should use indexed addressing. The program should reside in the lower RAM addresses.

18. When you are sure your program is correct, load it into the ET-3400 Trainer. Verify that you loaded it correctly; then execute it using the DO command.

19. Examine memory locations 0120_{16} through $01A0_{16}$. Each should be cleared. Examine locations below 0120_{16} and above $01A0_{16}$. These locations should not be cleared.

20. Debug your program if necessary and repeat steps 18 and 19 until the desired results are obtained.

DISCUSSION

Our solution to the problem is shown in Figure 62. Your solution may be similar or quite different. If it achieves the proper result and requires about the same number of bytes, then it is perfectly acceptable.

We still have not demonstrated the full power of indexed addressing because we have not yet used the offset capability. Let's look at how the offset capability can be used. Figure 63 shows three tables. The first two tables contain signed numbers, the third is initially cleared. The entries in the first two tables are to be added and the resulting sums are to be placed in the third table. That is, the first entry in table 1 is to be added to the first entry in table 2. The resulting sum is to be stored as the first entry of table 3. The second entry in table 1 is to be added to the second entry in table 2, forming the second entry in table 3; etc.

HEX ADDRESS	HEX CONTENTS	MNEMONICS/ CONTENTS	COMMENTS
0000	CE	LDX#	Load index register immediately with
0001	01	01	the address of the
0002	20	20	first location to be cleared.
0003	6F	CLR, X	Clear the location whose
0004	00	00	address is indicated by the index register.
0005	08	INX	Increment the index register.
0006	8C	CPX#	Compare the number in the index
0007	01	01	register with one greater than
0008	A1	A1	the address of the last location to be cleared.
0009	26	BNE	If there is no match
000A	F8	F8	branch back to here.
000B	3E	WAI	Otherwise, stop.

Figure 62

Program for clearing addresses 0120_{16}
through $01A0_{16}$.

TABLE 1		TABLE 2		TABLE 3	
ADDRESS	CONTENTS	ADDRESS	CONTENTS	ADDRESS	CONTENTS
0100	06	0110	FA	0150	00
0101	0F	0111	01	0151	00
0102	06	0112	1A	0152	00
0103	20	0113	10	0153	00
0104	2F	0114	11	0154	00
0105	00	0115	50	0155	00
0106	2F	0116	31	0156	00
0107	61	0117	0F	0157	00
0108	3E	0118	42	0158	00
0109	4F	0119	41	0159	00
010A	91	011A	0F	015A	00
010B	9F	011B	11	015B	00
010C	C0	011C	00	015C	00
010D	84	011D	4C	015D	00
010E	70	011E	70	015E	00
010F	E1	011F	0F	015F	00

Figure 63

Three tables.

PROCEDURE (Continued)

21. Enter the data shown in Figure 63 into the indicated addresses.

22. Write a program that will solve the problem described above.

23. Enter the program into the Trainer and execute it.

24. Examine addresses 0150_{16} through $015F_{16}$ to verify that the program performed properly.

25. If necessary, debug your program and try again.

DISCUSSION

The solution to the problem is shown in Figure 64.

HEX ADDRESS	HEX CONTENTS	MNEMONICS/ CONTENTS	COMMENTS
0000	CE	LDX#	Load index register with address
0001	01	01	of first entry
0002	00	00	in Table 1.
0003	A6	LDAA, X	Load entry from Table 1 into
0004	00	00	accumulator A.
0005	AB	ADDA, X	Add the corresponding entry from
0006	10	10	Table 2.
0007	A7	STAA, X	Store the result in the
0008	50	50	corresponding location in Table 3
0009	08	INX	Increment the index register.
000A	8C	CPX#	Compare the number in the index
000B	01	01	register with one greater
000C	10	10	than the address of the last entry in Table 1.
000D	26	BNE	If there is no match,
000E	F4	F4	branch to here.
000F	3E	WAI	Otherwise, stop.

Figure 64
Program for adding two tables.

Experiment 8

Arithmetic Operations

OBJECTIVES:

To gain practice using the instruction set and registers of the 6800 MPU.

To demonstrate a fast method of performing multiplication.

To demonstrate multiple-precision arithmetic.

To demonstrate an algorithm for finding the square root of a number.

To gain experience writing programs.

INTRODUCTION

In Unit 5, you were exposed to the full architecture and instruction set of the 6800 microprocessor. In this experiment, you will use some of the new-found capabilities of the microprocessor to solve some simple problems.

Mathematical operations make excellent programming examples and at the same time illustrate useful procedures. For these reasons, the programs developed in this experiment are concerned with arithmetic operations.

In an earlier unit, you learned that a computer can multiply by repeated addition. However, this is a very slow method of multiplication when large numbers are used.

A much faster method of multiplying involves a shifting-and-adding process. To illustrate the procedure, consider the long hand method of multiplying two 4-bit binary numbers. The procedure looks like this.

$$
\begin{array}{rcccc}
1101_2 & \leftarrow & \text{Multiplicand} & \rightarrow & 13_{10} \\
\underline{1011_2} & \leftarrow & \text{Multiplier} & \rightarrow & \underline{11_{10}} \\
1101 & & & & 13 \\
1101 & & & & \underline{13} \\
0000 & & & & 143_{10} \\
\underline{1101} & & & & \\
10001111_2 & \leftarrow & \text{Product} & &
\end{array}
$$

The decimal equivalents are shown for comparison purposes. The product is formed by shifting and adding the multiplicand. Put in computer terms, the procedure goes like this:

1. Clear the product.

2. Examine the multiplier. If it is 0, stop. Otherwise, go to 3.

3. Examine the LSB of the multiplier. If it is 1, add the multiplicand to the product then go to 4. If it is a 0, go to 4 without adding.

4. Shift the multiplicand to the left.

5. Shift the multiplier to the right so that the next bit becomes the LSB.

6. Go to 2.

PROCEDURE

1. Write a program of any length that will perform multiplication in the manner indicated. Here are some guidelines:

    A. You may use any of the instructions discussed up to this point.

    B. To keep the program simple, only unsigned 4-bit binary numbers are to be used for the multiplier and the multiplicand.

    C. The final product should be in Accumulator A when the multiplication is finished.

    D. The multiplier may be destroyed during the multiplication process.

    E. Assume that the multiplier and multiplicand are initially in memory. That is, you should load them into memory along with the program.

2. Try to write the program before you read further. If after 30 minutes, you feel you are not making progress, go on to step 3.

3. If you feel you need help, read over the following hints and then write the program.

    A. The product should be formed in accumulator A.

    B. The first step is to clear the product.

    C. The multiplicand is shifted and added to Accumulator A. Accumulator B is a good place to hold the multiplicand during this process.

    D. The multiplier can be tested for zero while still in memory by using the TST instruction followed by the BEQ instruction.

    E. A good way to test the LSB of the multiplier is to shift the multiplier one bit to the right into the carry flag and then test the carry flag with a BCC instruction.

4. Once your program is written, load it into the Trainer and run it. Verify that it works for several different values of multipliers and multiplicands. Debug your program as necessary.

DISCUSSION

The real test of your program is "Does it work?" If it works, then you have successfully completed this part of the experiment. One solution to the problem is shown in Figure 65. Compare your program with this one. If you could not write a successful program, study this program carefully to see how it handles each phase of the operation.

HEX ADDRESS	HEX CONTENTS	MNEMONICS/ CONTENTS	COMMENTS
0010	4F	CLRA	Set the product to 0.
0011	D6	LDAB	Load accumulator B with the
0012	22	22	multiplicand.
0013	7D	TST	Test
0014	00	00	the
0015	23	23	multiplier.
0016	27	BEQ	If it is 0, branch to the
0017	09	09	wait instruction.
0018	74	LSR	Shift the LSB of the
0019	00	00	multiplier to the
001A	23	23	right into the carry flag.
001B	24	BCC	If the carry flag is cleared
001C	01	01	skip the next instruction.
001D	1B	ABA	Add the multiplicand to the product.
001E	58	ASLB	Shift the multiplicand to the left.
001F	20	BRA	Branch back and go through again.
0020	F2	F2	
0021	3E	WAI	Wait.
0022	05	Multiplicand	
0023	03	Multiplier	

Figure 65
Multiplying by shifting and adding.

Obviously, this simple program has some serious drawbacks. The chief one is that the product cannot exceed eight bits. Fortunately, the basic procedure can be expanded so that much larger numbers can be handled. The solution is to use two bytes for the product. This will allow products up to $65,535_{10}$. In this example, the multiplier will be restricted to eight bits. However, the multiplicand can have up to 16 bits (two bytes) as long as the product does not exceed $65,535_{10}$. In an earlier unit, you learned that multiple-precision numbers can be added by a 2-step operation. The least significant (LS) byte of one number is added to the LS byte of the other. Then, the MS byte is added **with carry** to the MS byte of the other. Keep this in mind as you write your program.

The procedure for shifting a multiple-precision value will also come in handy. To shift a 2-byte number to the left, a 2-step procedure like that shown in Figure 66 can be used. First, the LS byte is shifted one place to the left into the carry bit by using the ASL instruction. Next the MS byte is rotated to the left. The result is that the 16-bit number has been shifted one bit to the left.

PROCEDURE (Continued)

5. Write a program that will multiply a double-precision multiplicand times an 8-bit multiplier. Assume that the double-precision product is to be stored in memory locations 0000_{16} and 0001_{16}. The double-precision multiplicand is initially in addresses 0002_{16} and 0003_{16}. The 8-bit multiplier is in address 0004_{16}.

6. Once again, you should try to write this program. If after 30 minutes or so you are not making progress, read the hints given in step 7.

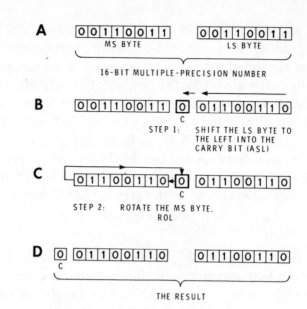

Figure 66
Shifting a multiple-precision number.

7. Read over the following hints (if necessary) and try again.

A. Initially clear both bytes of the product.

B. Test the multiplier for zero exactly as you did in the previous program.

C. Test the LSB of the multiplier as you did in the previous program.

D. When adding the multiplicand to the product, use the multiple-precision add technique.

E. When shifting the multiplicand to the left, use the technique shown in Figure 66.

8. Once your program is written, load it into the Trainer and verify that it works properly. Debug the program as necessary.

DISCUSSION

There are dozens of ways in which this program could be written. If your program produces proper results, then you have been successful. One solution to the problem is shown in Figure 67. Compare your program with this one. If you were unsuccessful in writing a program, study Figure 67 very carefully until you understand the procedures involved.

HEX ADDRESS	HEX CONTENTS	MNEMONICS/ CONTENTS	COMMENTS
0000	—	—	Product (LS byte)
0001	—	—	Product (MS byte)
0002	—	—	Multiplicand (LS byte)
0003	—	—	Multiplicand (MS byte)
0004	—	—	Multiplier
*	*	*	Instructions start at address 0010
0010	7F	CLR	Clear the product.
0011	00	00	
0012	00	00	
0013	7F	CLR	
0014	00	00	
0015	01	01	
0016	7D	TST	Test the multiplier.
0017	00	00	
0018	04	04	
0019	27	BEQ	If the multiplier is 0, branch to
001A	19	19	the WAI instruction.
001B	74	LSR	Otherwise, shift the right most
001C	00	00	bit of the multiplier into
001D	04	04	the C flag.
001E	24	BCC	If the C flag is 0 branch to
001F	0C	0C	here.
0020	96	LDAA	Otherwise, load the LS byte of
0021	00	00	the product into accumulator A.
0022	9B	ADDA	Then add the LS byte of the
0023	02	02	multiplicand.
0024	D6	LDAB	Load the MS byte of the product
0025	01	01	into accumulator B.
0026	D9	ADCB	Add (with carry) the MS byte of the
0027	03	03	multiplicand.
0028	97	STAA	Store the contents of accumulator A
0029	00	00	as the LS byte of the product.
002A	D7	STAB	Store the contents of accumulator B
002B	01	01	as the MS byte of the product.
002C	78	ASL	Shift the LS byte of the
002D	00	00	multiplicand to the left.
002E	02	02	
002F	79	ROL	Rotate the MS byte of the
0030	00	00	multiplicand to the left.
0031	03	03	
0032	20	BRA	Repeat the process.
0033	E2	E2	
0034	3E	WAI	Stop.

Figure 67

Program for multiplying a double-precision multiplicand by an 8-bit multiplier.

Another problem that makes a good programming exercise is finding the square root of a number. Writing the program is not too difficult once you develop the proper algorithm. While there are many different ways to find the square root of a number, the easiest method from the programmer's point of view involves the subtraction of successive odd integers.

This method works because of the relationship between perfect squares. The first several perfect squares are $0^2 = 0, 1^2 = 1, 2^2 = 4, 3^2 = 9, 4^2 = 16, 5^2 = 25$, etc. Notice:

The relationship between the numbers 0, 1, 4, 9, 16, 25, etc.

The difference between 0 and 1 is 1, the first odd integer.

The difference between 1 and 4 is 3, the second odd integer.

The difference between 4 and 9 is 5, the third odd integer; etc.

This relationship gives us a simple method of finding the exact square root of perfect squares and of approximating the square root of non-perfect squares.

The procedure for finding the square root of a number looks like this:

1. Subtract successive odd integers (1, 3, 5, 7, 9, etc.) from the number until the number is reduced to 0 or a negative value.

2. Count the number of subtractions required. The count is the exact square root of the number if the number was a perfect square. The count is the approximate square root if the number was not a perfect square.

For example, let's find the square root of 49_{10}.

49	Original Number.
$\underline{-1}$	Subtract the first odd integer.
48	
$\underline{-3}$	Subtract the second odd integer.
45	
$\underline{-5}$	Subtract the third odd integer.
40	
$\underline{-7}$	Subtract the fourth odd integer.
33	
$\underline{-9}$	Subtract the fifth odd integer.
24	
$\underline{-11}$	Subtract the sixth odd integer.
13	
$\underline{-13}$	Subtract the seventh odd integer.
0	Stop subtracting because the original number has been reduced to 0.

We simply count the number of subtractions required.

Since 7 subtractions were required, the square root of 49 is 7.

PROCEDURE (Continued)

9. With pencil and paper, use the above algorithm to find the square root of 81_{10}. Does the answer give the exact square? _____. Was the result of the final subtraction 0? _____.

10. With pencil and paper, use the above algorithm to find the square root of 119_{10}. How many subtractions are required to reduce the number to a negative value. Does this count approximate the square root of 119_{10}? _____.

11. Write a program that uses the above algorithm to find or approximate the square root of any unsigned 8-bit number.

12. Load your program into the Trainer and run it. Verify that it works for several different values.

DISCUSSION

Our solution to the problem is shown in Figure 68. The number is loaded into accumulator A, where it will be gradually reduced to a negative value. The odd integer is maintained in accumulator B. Each new odd integer is formed by incrementing twice. The SBA instruction is used to subtract the odd integer from the number. The BCS instruction is used to determine when the number goes negative (a borrow occurs at that point). You could have used the BMI instruction but this would limit the original number to a value below $+128_{10}$. A few bytes are saved by not maintaining a separate count of the number of subtractions. Instead, the final odd integer value is converted to the count. This is possible because of the relationship between the odd integer value and the number of subtractions. As the program is written, the final odd integer is always one more than twice the number of subtractions. By shifting the final odd integer to the right, the correct count is created.

HEX ADDRESS	HEX CONTENTS	MNEMONICS/ CONTENTS	COMMENTS
0000	96	LDAA	Load the number that is at
0001	0F	0F	this address into accumulator A.
0002	C6	LDAB#	Load accumulator B with the
0003	01	01	first odd integer.
0004	10	SBA	Subtract the odd integer from the number.
0005	25	BCS	If the carry is set, branch
0006	04	04	to here.
0007	5C	INCB	Otherwise, form the next higher odd
0008	5C	INCB	integer by incrementing B twice.
0009	20	BRA	Branch back
000A	F9	F9	to here.
000B	54	LSRB	Shift the odd integer to the right.
000C	D7	STAB	Store the answer at
000D	10	10	this address.
000E	3E	WAI	Wait.
000F	—	Number	Number to be operated upon.
0010	—	Answer	Final answer appears here.

Figure 68
Square root subroutine.

Of course, any square root program that is limited to numbers below 256_{10} is of limited use. However, this same technique can be applied to multiple-precision numbers. Figure 69 shows a program that can find or approximate the square root of numbers up to $16,385_{10}$. Before you study this program, try to write your own program to do this.

HEX ADDRESS	HEX CONTENTS	MNEMONICS/ CONTENTS	COMMENTS
0000	96	LDAA	Load accumulator A with the
0001	1A	1A	LS byte of the number.
0002	D6	LDAB	Load accumulator B with the
0003	19	19	MS byte of the number.
0004	7F	CLR	Clear
0005	00	00	the odd
0006	1B	1B	integer.
0007	7C	INC	Increment.
0008	00	00	the odd
0009	1B	1B	integer.
000A	90	SUBA	Subtract the odd
000B	1B	1B	integer from the LS byte of the number.
000C	C2	SBCB#	Take care of any borrow
000D	00	00	from the MS byte of the number.
000E	25	BCS	If the carry is set, branch
000F	05	05	to here.
0010	7C	INC	Otherwise, form the next
0011	00	00	higher odd integer by
0012	1B	1B	incrementing
0013	20	BRA	and branching
0014	F2	F2	to here.
0015	74	LSR	Convert the odd integer to
0016	00	00	the answer by shifting
0017	1B	1B	right.
0018	3E	WAI	Stop.
0019	—	Number (MS)	Number to be
001A	—	Number (LS)	operated upon.
001B	—	Odd integer	Form the odd integer and the answer here.

Figure 69
Routine for finding the square root of a
double precision number.

Experiment 9

Stack Operations

OBJECTIVES:

> *To demonstrate the stack operations that occur automatically.*

> *To demonstrate ways that the programmer can use the stack.*

> *To demonstrate the break-point capability of the Trainer.*

INTRODUCTION

As you learned in Unit 6, the stack is used by the MPU to perform some automatic functions. When an interrupt occurs or a WAI is encountered, the MPU pushes the contents of the program counter, index register, accumulators, and condition codes on to the stack. We can easily verify this.

PROCEDURE

1. Figure 70 shows a program for setting the MPU registers to a known state. Examine the program and determine the hex contents of the following registers immediately after the WAI is executed.

> Condition Code Register   _____
> Accumulator B   _____
> Accumulator A   _____
> Index Register   _____
> Program Counter   _____

HEX ADDRESS	HEX CONTENTS	MNEMONICS/ CONTENTS	COMMENTS
0000	8E	LDS#	Load 0020 into
0001	00	00	the stack pointer
0002	20	20	
0003	CE	LDX#	Load EEDD into the index register.
0004	EE	EE	
0005	DD	DD	
0006	C6	LDAB#	Load BB into ACCB.
0007	BB	BB	
0008	86	LDAA#	Load AA into ACCA.
0009	AA	AA	
000A	36	PSHA	Push AA onto the stack.
000B	86	LDAA#	Load CC into ACCA.
000C	CC	CC	
000D	06	TAP	Transfer CC into the condition codes.
000E	32	PULA	Pull AA from the stack.
000F	3E	WAI	Wait.
0010			

Figure 70

This routine sets the contents of all MPU
registers to known values.

2. Load the program into the Trainer and verify that you loaded it properly.

3. Execute the program using the DO command.

4. Examine the following memory locations and record their hex contents.

Address	Contents	Register
001A	_____	_____
001B	_____	_____
001C	_____	_____
001D	_____	_____
001E	_____	_____
001F	_____	_____
0020	_____	_____

5. Identify the register from which these numbers came.

6. Try to examine the contents of ACCA, ACCB, PC, SP, and INDEX register. Do their contents agree with the number loaded there?

DISCUSSION

When the WAI instruction is executed, the contents of the MPU registers are pushed onto the stack. Since the stack pointer is initially at 0020, the contents of the registers are stored as follows.

Address	Contents	Where it came from
001A	CC	Condition Codes
001B	BB	Accumulator B
001C	AA	Accumulator A
001D	EE	Index Register (high byte)
001E	DD	Index Register (low byte)
001F	00	Program Counter (high byte)
0020	10	Program Counter (low byte)

When you tried to examine the contents of ACCA, ACCB, SP, etc., you found that their contents did not agree with what was loaded. The reason for this **apparent** error is that the Trainer does not actually examine the contents of these registers. Instead, it examines what is placed in the stack by the WAI instruction. However, when the Trainer is reset, the monitor program assumes that the stack starts at address 00D1. Since our program moved the location of the stack, we can not use the ACCA, ACCB, PC, SP, CC, or INDEX commands after changing the stack pointer and then resetting the Trainer.

This demonstrates how the MPU uses the stack. A similar operation occurs for the SWI instruction or when a hardware interrupt occurs. Of course, the programmer can also use the stack.

PROCEDURE (Continued)

7. Figure 71 shows a program that will clear memory locations 0001 through 001F. It then transfers a list of numbers to these addresses. The numbers come from addresses 0151 through 016F.

HEX ADDRESS	HEX CONTENTS	MNEMONICS/ ADDRESS	COMMENTS
0020	CE	LDX#	Load the index register
0021	00	00	with highest
0022	1F	1F	address to be cleared.
0023	6F	CLR, X	Clear it.
0024	00	00	
0025	09	DEX	Decrement index register to next lower address.
0026	26	BNE	Finished? If not, go back and
0027	FB	FB	clear the indicated address.
0028	08	INX	Set index register to first entry in new list.
0029	8E	LDS#	Set the stack pointer to one less than
002A	01	01	the first entry in the old list.
002B	50	50	
002C	32	PULA	Pull the entry from the old list.
002D	A7	STAA, X	Store it in the new list.
002E	00	00	
002F	08	INX	Increment index register to next entry in list.
0030	8C	CPX#	Finished?
0031	00	00	
0032	20	20	
0033	26	BNE	If not, go back and pull next entry.
0034	F7	F7	
0035	3E	WAI	Otherwise, wait.

Figure 71

Program for demonstrating stack operations and breakpoints.

8. Load this program into the Trainer and verify that you loaded it properly.

9. At address 0151 through 016F, load the numbers 01 through $1F_{16}$, respectively.

10. Execute the program using the DO command.

11. Examine addresses 0001 through 001F. They should contain the numbers 01 through 1F, respectively.

DISCUSSION

This illustrates how the stack can be used in conjunction with indexing to move a list of numbers.

When this program is executed using the DO command, everything happens so fast that it is impossible to see intermediate results. Of course, you could use the single-step mode and examine the result produced by every single instruction. But in many programs, this is a long, tedious process. Therefore, the Trainer provides another way to examine programs. It allows us to set four different breakpoints in our program. The Trainer will execute instructions at its normal speed until it reaches one of these breakpoints. At that point, the Trainer will stop with the address and op code of the next instruction displayed. While the Trainer is stopped, you can examine and change the contents of any register or memory location. When you are ready to resume, you depress the return (RTI) key and the Trainer executes instructions at its normal speed until the next breakpoint or a WAI instruction is encountered.

PROCEDURE (Continued)

12. Verify that the program is still in memory.

13. Depress the RESET key. Do not depress RESET again as you perform the following steps. To do so will erase any breakpoints that you set.

14. Refer to the program listing in Figure 71. Let's assume we wish to stop and examine memory and the MPU registers just before the BNE instruction at address 0026 is executed.

15. Depress the BR key. The display should be _ _ _ _ Br. The Trainer is now ready to accept the first breakpoint address. Enter the address at which the Trainer is to stop: 0026. The breakpoint is now entered.

16. Without hitting RESET, depress the DO key. Enter the address of the first instruction in the program: 0020.

17. Immediately, the display will show the address 0026 and op code 26 at which the breakpoint occurred.

18. Without hitting RESET, examine the contents of the index register. It should now read 001E.

19. Depress the EXAM key and examine address 001F. It should now be cleared.

20. Notice that you can examine the contents of any MPU register or memory location from this breakpoint mode.

21. When you are ready for the program to resume, depress the RTI key once. Again, the display will read 002626 because the MPU is back at the same breakpoint on the second pass through the first loop.

22. Examine the index register again. It should now read 001D. Examine location 001E and verify that it has been cleared.

23. The loop will be repeated 31_{10} times. On the 32nd pass, the program will escape the loop.

24. Before you go further, set a second breakpoint at the INX instruction. Do this by depressing the BR key and entering the address of the instruction (0028).

25. Depress the RTI key again. Notice that the program is still stopping at the first breakpoint. It will continue to do so until it escapes the first loop.

26. You have now pushed the RTI key three times. Repeatedly push the RTI key until the display changes to 0028 08. The RTI key should have been depressed a total of 32_{10} times, counting the first three times.

27. The program is now waiting at the second break point.

28. To demonstrate a point, let's set two additional break points.

29. Depress the BR key and enter address 0029. This sets the third break point at the LDS# instruction.

30. Depress the BR key again and enter address 0033. This sets the fourth break point at the last BNE instruction.

31. The Trainer will accept only four breakpoints. We have now reached this limit. Depress the BR key again in an attempt to enter a fifth breakpoint. Notice that the word "FULL!" appears on the display.

32. Depress the RTI key so that the Trainer resumes program execution. It should stop at the third breakpoint.

33. Depress the RTI key again. The program should stop at the fourth breakpoint. Notice that the program is again in a loop. On each pass through the loop, the program will stop at this fourth breakpoint.

34. Analyze the operation of the program by examining the pertinent registers and memory locations on each pass through the loop.

DISCUSSION

The breakpoint capability of the Trainer can be a powerful aid in writing, analyzing and debugging a program. It allows us to stop at four distinct points in the program. Here are some tips to remember when using this capability:

1. A maximum of four breakpoints can be used.

2. These may be entered all at once or during a previous breakpoint pause.

3. The RESET key erases all breakpoints.

4. The contents of the address at which the breakpoint is set must be an op code.

Experiment 10

Subroutines

OBJECTIVES:

To demonstrate the use of subroutines.

To demonstrate that the monitor program of the ET-3400 Trainer contains some useful subroutines that can be called when needed.

To gain experience writing programs.

INTRODUCTION

Most of the subroutines that you will develop and use in this experiment deal with lighting the displays on the Trainer. For this reason, we will begin by discussing how the displays are accessed.

The ET-3400 Microprocessor Trainer has six hexadecimal displays. Each display contains eight light-emitting diodes (LED's) arranged as shown in Figure 72. Each LED is given two addresses. The addresses for the left-most display are shown. To light a particular LED, we simply store an odd number at the proper address. An odd number is used because the LED responds to a 1 in bit 0 of the byte that is stored. To turn an LED off, we store an even number at the proper address. The following procedure will demonstrate this.

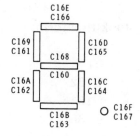

Figure 72
Addresses of the various segments in the
left LED display.

PROCEDURE

1. Write a program that will halt after storing an odd number (such as 01) at address C167$_{16}$.

2. Load the program into the Trainer and execute it using the DO command. The microprocessor should halt with the decimal point of the left-most display lit.

3. Notice that the LED remains lit until it is deliberately turned off.

DISCUSSION

To form characters, the LED's in the display must be turned on in combination. For example, to form the letter "A", the segments at addresses C162, C161, C166, C165, C164, and C160 must be turned on.

PROCEDURE (Continued)

4. Write a program that will halt after storing an odd number (such as 01) at the six addresses listed above.

5. Load the program into the Trainer and execute it using the DO command. The microprocessor should halt with the letter A in the left-most display.

DISCUSSION

Your program probably took this form:

```
LDAA    #       01
STAA            C162
STAA            C161
STAA            C166
            •
            •
            •
WAI
```

While this approach works, the program would have to be rewritten for each new character. What is needed is a program that will form many characters. One approach is to store characters as 8-bit character bytes. Since there are eight LED's in each display, each bit of the character byte can be assigned to a different LED segment. Figure 73A shows how each bit in a character byte is assigned to each segment of the display. To light a corresponding LED, the proper bit in the character byte must be 1. For example, Figure 73B shows the character byte for the letter A. To form this letter, all display segments except C163 and C167 must be lit. Therefore, a 1 is placed in the character byte at all bits except the two that correspond to these addresses.

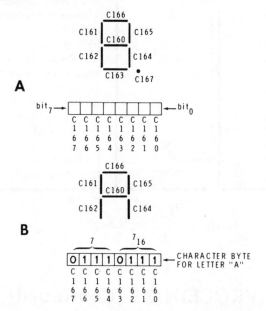

Figure 73

Assigning the bits of the character byte.

The display responds only to bit 0 of the character byte. To make each segment bit appear in turn at bit 0, the character byte must be shifted to the right. After each shift, the contents of the character byte must be stored at the address whose corresponding bit is now at bit 0. The procedure is:

1. Store the contents of the character byte at $C160_{16}$.

2. Shift the character byte to the right.

3. Store it at $C161_{16}$.

4. Shift it to the right again.

5. Store it at $C162_{16}$.

     Etc.

A program that will do this is shown in Figure 74.

HEX ADDRESS	HEX CONTENTS	MNEMONIC/ CONTENTS	COMMENTS
0000	86	LDAA#	Load accumulator A immediate with the
0001	77	77	character byte.
0002	CE	LDX#	Load the index register immediate with
0003	C1	C1	the address.
0004	60	60	of the left display.
0005	A7	STAA, X	Store the character byte at the
0006	00	00	address indicated by the index register.
0007	44	LSRA	Shift the character bit to the right.
0008	08	INX	Advance index register to the address of the next segment.
0009	8C	CPX	Compare index register with one greater
000A	C1	C1	than the address of the
000B	68	68	last segment.
000C	26	BNE	If no match occurs branch
000D	F7	F7	back to here.
000E	3E	WAI	Otherwise, stop.

Figure 74
Program for lighting a display.

PROCEDURE (Continued)

6.   Load the program into the Trainer and verify that you loaded it correctly.

7.   Execute the program using the DO command. The left-most digit should display the letter A.

8.   The character byte is at address 0001. Change this byte to 47_{16}.

9.   Execute the program again using the DO command. What letter appears in the display? _____.

10.   Change the character byte so that the letter H is displayed. What character byte is required? _____.

11.   Change the character byte to 79_{16}. Execute the program. What character is displayed? _____.

12.   Refer to Figure 75. This figure shows the addresses of the LED's in each of the six displays. You have seen that the left display has an address of $C16X_{16}$. The X stands for some number between 0 and F, depending on which segment of that display we wish to use. The next display to the right has an address of $C15X_{16}$; etc.

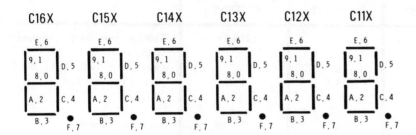

Figure 75

Addresses of the various display segments.

13.   Now return to the program shown in Figure 74. Addresses 0003 and 0004 contain the address of the affected display. By changing this address, we can move the character to a different display. Actually since all display addresses start with C1, we need only change the number at address 0004.

14.   Change the byte at 0004 to 50_{16}. Change the byte at $000B_{16}$ to 58. Execute the program using the DO command. The character should appear in the second display from the left.

15.   Change the byte at 0004 to 10_{16} and the byte at 000B to 18_{16}. Execute the program using the DO command. The character should appear in the right-most display.

DISCUSSION

It has probably occurred to you that the monitor program must have a subroutine that performs this same function. Fortunately, this subroutine is written in such a way that we can use it. It is called OUTCH for OUTput CHaracter. It starts at address $FE3A_{16}$. We can call this subroutine anytime we like by using the JSR instruction. This subroutine assumes that the character byte is in accumulator A.

PROCEDURE

16. Load the program shown in Figure 76. Verify that you loaded it properly.

HEX ADDRESS	HEX CONTENTS	MNEMONICS/ CONTENTS	COMMENTS
0000	86	LDAA#	Load accumulator A immediate with the
0001	37	37	character byte for the letter H.
0002	BD	JSR	Jump to subroutine
0003	FE	FE	OUTCH
0004	3A	3A	
0005	86	LDAA#	Load ACCA with
0006	4F	4F	next character byte.
0007	BD	JSR	
0008	FE	FE	Display it.
0009	3A	3A	
000A	86	LDAA#	Load next character.
000B	0E	0E	
000C	BD	JSR	
000D	FE	FE	Display it.
000E	3A	3A	
000F	86	LDAA#	Load next character.
0010	67	67	
0011	BD	JSR	
012	FE	FE	Display it.
0013	3A	3A	
0014	3E	WAI	Stop.

Figure 76

This program uses the OUTCH subroutine in the monitor program to display
a message.

17. Execute the program using the DO command. What message does the program write? _____.

18. Notice that each character is written in a different display. Thus, the subroutine OUTCH automatically changes the address to that of the next display after each character is written.

DISCUSSION

The monitor program writes several messages of its own. Examples are: ACCA, ACCB, CPU UP, and FULL! Thus, the monitor has a subroutine that can be used to write messages. It is called OUTSTR for OUTput a STRing of characters. Its starting address is at FE52$_{16}$. There is a special convention for calling this subroutine. The JSR FE52$_{16}$ instruction must be followed immediately by the character bytes that make up the message. Up to six characters can be displayed. The last character must have the decimal point lit. After the message is displayed, control is returned to the instruction immediately following the last character.

PROCEDURE (Continued)

19. Load the program shown in Figure 77 into the Trainer and verify that you loaded it properly.

HEX ADDRESS	HEX CONTENTS	MNEMONIC/ CONTENTS	COMMENTS
0000	BD	JSR	Jump to the subroutine that
0001	FE	FE	will display the following message.
0002	52	52	
0003	37	37	H
0004	4F	4F	E
0005	0E	0E	L
0006	E7	E7	P. ◄ Decimal point must be lit in last character.
0007	3E	WAI	Then stop.

Figure 77
The OUTSTR subroutine in the monitor is
used to display a message.

20. Execute the program using the DO command. What message does it display? _____.

21. Modify the program so that it displays HELLO.

HEX ADDRESS	HEX CONTENTS	MNEMONICS/ CONTENTS	COMMENTS
0000	BD	JSR	
0001	FE	FE	Cal OUTSTR.
0002	52	52	
0003	76	76	N
0004	FE	FE	O. ← Decimal point lit (last character).
0005	BD	JSR	
0006	FE	FE	Call OUTSTR again.
0007	52	52	
0008	5E	5E	G
0009	FE	FE	O. ← Decimal point lit (last character).
000A	3E	WAI	Then stop.

Figure 78
OUTSTR is called twice.

22. The program shown in Figure 78 calls the OUTSTR subroutine twice. Load this program into the Trainer.

23. Execute it using the DO command. What message is displayed? _____.

24. Notice that the second message (GO.) is written to the right of the first. Thus, subroutine OUTSTR does not reset the display to the left for the second message.

25. Rewrite the program so that two blank displays appear between NO. and GO.

DISCUSSION

When displaying long messages such as: "HELLO CAN I HELP YOU?", the display must be given no more than six characters at a time. Also, a short delay must be placed between the various parts of the message. A delay of over one second can be achieved by loading the index register with FFFF and decrementing it to 0000. We can write a display subroutine and call it between each part of the message.

Also, because we are using the same displays over again for each part of the message, each new word should start on the left. The subroutine called OUTSTR has an alternate entry point at address $FD8C_{16}$ called OUTSTJ. The calling convention for this subroutine is the same as that for OUTSTR. However, each new message starts in the left-most display.

PROCEDURE (Continued)

26. Load the program shown in Figure 79. Verify that you loaded it properly.

27. Execute the program using the DO command. What message is displayed? _____.

28. Change the number in address 0030_{16} to 40_{16}.

29. Execute the program using the DO command. What affect does this have?

30. Write a program of your own that will display "LOAD 2 IS BAD."

DISCUSSION

The monitor program in the Trainer contains some other useful subroutines. These are outlined in the manual for the ET-3400 Microprocessor Trainer. Two of the most useful are REDIS and OUTBYT.

OUTBYT is a subroutine that displays the contents of accumulator A as two hex digits. Its address is $FE20_{16}$. When this subroutine is called for the first time, the two left displays are used. If it is called again without being reset, the two center displays are used. The third time, the two right displays are used.

The display can be reset to the left by calling the REDIS subroutine. This subroutine is located in address $FCBC_{16}$. If OUTBYT is called after REDIS is called, the two left displays will be used.

HEX ADDRESS	HEX CONTENTS	MNEMONICS/ CONTENTS	COMMENTS
0000	BD	JSR	
0001	FD	FD	Call OUTSTJ.
0002	8C	8C	
0003	37	37	H
0004	4F	4F	E
0005	0E	0E	L
0006	0E	0E	L
0007	FE	FE	O.
0008	BD	JSR	
0009	00	00	Call Delay Subroutine
000A	2F	2F	
000B	BD	JSR	
000C	FD	FD	Call OUTSTJ again.
000D	8C	8C	
000E	4E	4E	C
000F	77	77	A
0010	76	76	N
0011	00	00	blank
0012	B0	B0	I.
0013	BD	JSR.	
0014	00	00	Call Delay Subroutine
0015	2F	2F	
0016	BD	JSR	
0017	FD	FD	Call OUTSTJ again.
0018	8C	8C	
0019	37	37	H
001A	4F	4F	E
001B	0E	0E	L
001C	67	67	P
001D	80	80	•
001E	BD	JSR	Call Delay Subroutine
001F	00	00	
0020	2F	2F	
0021	BD	JSR	Call OUTSTJ again.
0022	FD	FD	
0023	8C	8C	
0024	3B	3B	Y
0025	7E	7E	O
0026	3E	3E	U
0027	00	00	blank
0028	80	80	•
0029	BD	JSR	
002A	00	00	
002B	2F	2F	
002C	7E	JMP	Do it all again.
002D	00	00	
002E	00	00	
002F	CE	LDX#	
0030	FF	FF	
0031	FF	FF	Delay subroutine.
0032	09	DEX	
0033	26	BNE	
0034	FD	FD	
0035	39	RTS	

Figure 79

This program makes extensive use of the
subroutine call.

PROCEDURE (Continued)

31. Load the program shown in Figure 80. Verify that you loaded it properly.

Figure 80

Using the OUTBYT and REDIS subroutines.

HEX ADDRESS	HEX CONTENTS	MNEMONICS/ CONTENTS	COMMENTS
0000	4F	CLRA	Clear accumulator A
0001	BD	JSR	
0002	FE	FE	Call OUTBYT
0003	20	20	
0004	BD	JSR	
0005	00	00	Call Delay Subroutine
0006	0E	0E	
0007	4C	INCA	Increment accumulator A
0008	BD	JSR	
0009	FC	FC	Call REDIS
000A	BC	BC	
000B	7E	JMP	
000C	00	00	Do it again.
000D	01	01	
000E	CE	LDX#	
000F	FF	FF	
0010	FF	FF	
0011	09	DEX	Delay Subroutine.
0012	26	BNE	
0013	FD	FD	
0014	39	RTS	

32. Execute the program using the DO command.

33. Which digits are used by the display? _____.

34. Notice that the JSR instruction at address 0008 calls the subroutine that resets the display to the left.

35. To illustrate why this is necessary, let's see what happens when this important step is omitted. Change the contents of locations 0008, 0009, and 000A to 01. This replaces the JSR instruction with three NOPs.

36. Execute the program using the DO command. Notice that, without calling the REDIS subroutine, the display advances to the right and is lost after the third time through the loop.

37. Restore the program to its original state. How can the count be speeded up?

DISCUSSION

The speed of the count can be varied by changing the contents of addresses 000F and 0010. It probably has occurred to you that the trainer could be turned into a digital clock. In the following procedure, you will develop a program that will do this.

PROCEDURE

38. Write a program that will count seconds from 00 to 99_{10}. The seconds count should be maintained in the two left-most displays. It should count as the above program did, but in decimal instead of hexadecimal.

39. If you have problems, remember that the DAA instruction can be used to convert the addition of BCD numbers to a BCD sum. However, the DAA instruction works only if preceeded immediately by an ADDA or ADCA instruction.

40. Load your program into the Trainer and execute it using the DO command.

DISCUSSION

One solution is shown in Figure 81. Carefully study this program. This routine counts the seconds in decimal. However in a real digital clock, the seconds reset to 00 after 59_{10} rather than after 99_{10}.

HEX ADDRESS	HEX CONTENTS	MNEMONICS/ CONTENTS	COMMENTS
0000	4F	CLRA	Clear seconds.
0001	BD	JSR	
0002	FE	FE	Call OUTBYT
0003	20	20	
0004	BD	JSR	
0005	00	00	Call Delay subroutine
0006	10	10	
0007	8B	ADDA#	Increment seconds
0008	01	01	
0009	19	DAA	Make it decimal
000A	BD	JSR	
000B	FC	FC	Call REDIS
000C	BC	BC	
000D	7E	JMP	
000E	00	00	Do it all again.
000F	01	01	
0010	CE	LDX#	
0011	C5	C5	
0012	00	00	One second
0013	09	DEX	Delay Subroutine
0014	26	BNE	
0015	FD	FD	
0016	39	RTS	

Figure 81

This routine counts seconds from 00 to 99.

PROCEDURE (Continued)

41. Modify your program (or the one in this Experiment) so that it displays seconds from 00 to 59 and then returns to 00 and starts over again.

42. Load your program into the Trainer and execute it using the DO command.

43. Debug your program if necessary until it performs properly.

DISCUSSION

One solution is shown in Figure 82. The seconds count is compared to 60 each time it is incremented. When it reaches 60, it is reset to 00.

HEX ADDRESS	HEX CONTENTS	MNEMONICS/ CONTENTS	COMMENTS
0000	C6	LDAB#	Load number for comparison
0001	60	60	
0002	4F	CLRA	Clear seconds.
0003	BD	JSR	
0004	FE	FE	Call OUTBYT
0005	20	20	
0006	BD	JSR	
0007	00	00	Call Delay Subroutine
0008	14	14	
0009	BD	JSR	
000A	FC	FC	Call REDIS
000B	BC	BC	
000C	8B	ADDA#	Increment seconds.
000D	01	01	
000E	19	DAA	Make it decimal
000F	11	CBA	Time to clear seconds
0010	27	BEQ	Yes.
0011	F0	F0	
0012	20	BRA	No.
0013	EF	EF	
0014	CE	LDX#	
0015	C5	C5	
0016	00	00	One second
0017	09	DEX	Delay Subroutine
0018	26	BNE	
0019	FD	FD	
001A	39	RTS	

Figure 82

This routine counts seconds from 00 to 59.

The next step is to add a minutes count. This can be done by incrementing a decimal number each time the seconds count "rolls over" from 59 to 00. The decimal number is then displayed as minutes.

PROCEDURE (Continued)

44. Write a program that will display minutes and seconds properly. The minutes should be displayed in the two left displays; the seconds in the two center displays. Like the seconds, the minutes should return to 00 after 59.

45. Load your program and execute it.

46. Debug your program as necessary.

DISCUSSION

A solution is shown in Figure 83. Your approach may be more straightforward, but may require more memory.

The final step is to include the hours display.

PROCEDURE (Continued)

47. Modify your program so that it displays hours, minutes and seconds.

48. Load your program and execute it.

49. Debug your program as necessary.

HEX ADDRESS	HEX CONTENTS	MNEMONICS/ CONTENTS	COMMENTS
0000	00	00	Reserved for seconds
0001	00	00	Reserved for minutes
0002	CE	LDX#	
0003	C5	C5	
0004	00	00	One second
0005	09	DEX	delay.
0006	26	BNE	
0007	FD	FD	
0008	C6	LDAB#	Load number for comparison.
0009	60	60	
000A	0D	SEC	Set carry bit.
000B	8D	BSR	Branch to subroutine to
000C	11	11	increment seconds.
000D	8D	BSR	Branch to the same subroutine
000E	0F	0F	to increment minutes.
000F	BD	JSR	
0010	FC	FC	Call REDIS
0011	BC	BC	
0012	96	LDAA	Load minutes
0013	01	01	
0014	BD	JSR	
0015	FE	FE	Call OUTBYT to
0016	20	20	display minutes.
0017	96	LDAA	Load seconds
0018	00	00	
0019	BD	JSR	Call OUTBYT to
001A	FE	FE	display seconds
001B	20	20	
001C	20	BRA	Do it all again.
001D	E4	E4	
001E	A6	LDAA, X	Load seconds (or minutes) into A.
001F	00	00	
0020	89	ADCA#	Increment if necessary
0021	00	00	
0022	19	DAA	Adjust to decimal
0023	11	CBA	Time to clear?
0024	26	BNE	No.
0025	01	01	
0026	4F	CLRA	Yes.
0027	A7	STAA, X	Store seconds (or minutes)
0028	00	00	
0029	08	INX	
002A	07	TPA	
002B	88	EORA#	Complement carry bit
002C	01	01	
002D	06	TAP	
002E	39	RTS	

Increment subroutine

Figure 83

Routine for displaying minutes and seconds.

DISCUSSION

A solution is shown in Figure 84. This program evolved over a period of time and is extremely compact. It is virtually impossible for a beginning programmer to write a program this compact on the first try. Your program may require substantially more memory, but the important thing is: does it work?

While you can "fine tune" the clock period by changing the numbers in addresses 0004 and 0005, the clock will never be very accurate because it is temperature sensitive. In a later experiment, you will rectify this problem and produce an extremely accurate clock.

HEX ADDRESS	HEX CONTENTS	MNEMONICS/ CONTENTS	COMMENTS	
0000	00	00	Reserved for seconds	
0001	00	00	Reserved for minutes	
0002	00	00	Reserved for hours	
0003	CE	LDX#	⎫	
0004	C5	C5	⎪	
00Q5	00	00	⎬ One second	
0006	09	DEX	⎪ Delay	
0007	26	BNE	⎪	
0008	FD	FD	⎭	
0009	C6	LDAB#	Minutes and seconds will	
000A	60	60	be compared with sixty.	
000B	0D	SEC	Prepare to increment seconds	
000C	8D	BSR	Go to subroutine that will	
000D	11	11	increment seconds.	
000E	8D	BSR	Go to same subroutine. It will increment	
000F	0F	0F	Minutes if necessary.	
0010	C6	LDAB#	Hours will be compared	
0011	12	12	with twelve.	
0012	8D	BSR	Go to same subroutine. It will increment	
0013	0B	0B	hours if necessary.	
0014	BD	JSR		
0015	FC	FC	Call REDIS	
0016	BC	BC		
0017	8D	BSR	Call display subroutine to display	
0018	17	17	hours.	
0019	8D	BSR	Call display subroutine to display	
001A	15	15	minutes.	
001B	8D	BSR	Call display subroutine to display	
001C	13	13	seconds.	
001D	20	BRA	Do it all again.	
001E	E4	E4		
001F	A6	LDAA, X	Load seconds (or minutes or hours).	⎫
0020	00	00		⎪
0021	89	ADCA#	Increment if necessary.	⎪
0022	00	00		⎪
0023	19	DAA	Adjust to decimal.	⎪
0024	11	CBA	Time to clear?	⎪
0025	25	BCS	No.	⎪
0026	01	01		⎪
0027	4F	CLRA	Yes.	Increment Subroutine
0028	A7	STAA, X	Store seconds (or minutes or hours).	⎪
0029	00	00		⎪
002A	08	INX	Point index register at minutes (or hours).	⎪
002B	07	TPA		⎪
002C	88	EORA#	Complement carry bit	⎪
002D	01	01		⎪
002E	06	TAP		⎪
002F	39	RTS		⎭
0030	09	DEX	Point index register at hours (or minutes or seconds)	⎫
0031	A6	LDAA, X	Load hours (or minutes or seconds)	⎪
0032	00	00		⎬ Display Subroutine
0033	7E	JSR	Display hours (or minutes or seconds)	⎪
0034	FE	FE		⎪
0035	20	20		⎪
0036	39	RTS		⎭

Figure 84

Twelve-hour clock program.

INTERFACING EXPERIMENTS

Introduction

This section contains nine interfacing experiments that are to be assembled and run on the Microprocessor Trainer. Most of the circuit parts for these experiments are supplied with this course. The remaining parts were part of the Trainer kit.

You will be instructed to perform these experiments at the end of Units 7 and 8. Do not confuse them with the programming experiments. When you complete an experiment, you will be directed to the next experiment, or back to the Unit Activity Guide of the unit that directed you to the experiment.

If your Trainer is Model Number ET-3400 and has been modified for use with the Heathkit Memory I/O Accessory, Model ETA-3400, disconnect the 40-pin plug that connects the Trainer to the Memory I/O Accessory. Then reinstall the 2112 RAM IC's at IC-14 through IC-17 before starting the experiments in this unit.

If your Trainer is Model Number ET-3400A and has been modified for use with the Heathkit Memory I/O Accessory, disconnect the 40-pin plug that connects the Trainer to the Memory I/O Accessory. Then reinstall the 2114 RAM IC's at IC-14 and IC-15 before starting the experiments in this unit.

Experiment 11

Memory Circuits

OBJECTIVES:

> *Show how memory circuits can be connected to a microprocessor.*
>
> *Demonstrate timing requirements when using memory circuits.*
>
> *Show how data is stored and read from memory circuits.*
>
> *Demonstrate an elementary memory test to ensure proper, reliable operation.*

INTRODUCTION

In this experiment, you will construct a memory on the large connector block of the Microprocessor Trainer and interface the circuit with the Trainer circuits.

The initial sections of the experiment will examine memory and its characteristics. The remaining experiment section will interface the memory with the microprocessor and its support circuits. This program and all remaining hardware experiment programs will use a computer print-out listing. A detailed explanation of how to read the listing will be given later in the experiment.

TRAINER POWER REVIEW

With the Trainer plugged in and the Power switch off, the display LED's and the +5, +12, and −12 volt connector blocks are disconnected from Trainer power. The single LED next to the Power switch indicates this condition. Whenever you make connections between the Trainer and the large connector block, **always** switch the power off. This will not disturb any program stored in the Trainer. If you must remove or install a component in the Trainer circuits, such as an IC, remove the power plug from the wall receptacle.

MATERIAL REQUIRED

1   ET-3400 Microprocessor Trainer

1   1000 ohm, 1/4-watt, 10% resistor

1   Pushbutton switch (#1)

1   7400 integrated circuit (443-1)

1   74126 integrated circuit (443-717)

1   74LS30 integrated circuit (443-732)

1   74LS27 integrated circuit (443-800)

Hookup wire (22 gauge, solid)

1   IC puller tool   } From Trainer
                                                                    Parts Package
Hookup wire (22 gauge, solid)

ADDITIONAL MATERIAL REQUIRED (TRAINER ET-3400A)

2   2112-2 IC's — 443-721

PROCEDURE

1. Turn the Trainer power off, then unplug your Trainer from its wall receptacle.

2. Insert the 74126 (443-717) and 7400 (443-1) integrated circuits (IC's) into the large connector block as shown in Figure 85. Always install an IC in the block with pin 1 toward the left.

NOTE: If you are using Trainer model number ET-3400, perform step 3. If your Trainer is an ET-3400A perform step 3A. All other steps of this procedure are common to both Trainer types, except where indicated.

3. Using the IC puller tool, remove the 2112 (443-721) IC from its socket at location IC17. (Observe the precautions described in Experiment 7 for MOS devices.) Then insert the IC into the large connector block as shown in Figure 85. This IC will be reinstalled in the Trainer in a later experiment.

3A. Locate a 2112-2 IC (Heath number 443-721) that was supplied with this Course. Notice that this IC is packaged in conductive foam.

NOTE: These IC's are rugged reliable components. However, normal static electricity discharged from your body through an IC pin to an object can damage the IC. Install these IC's without interruption as follows:

*   Remove the IC from its package with both hands.

*   Hold the IC with one hand and straighten any bent pins with the other hand.

*   Insert the IC into the large connector block as shown in Figures 85 and 86.

4. Install the pushbutton switch at the location shown in Figure 85. Be sure to press straight down when you insert the switch leads — they are fragile.

5. Using the 22 gauge, solid hookup wire, interconnect the IC's and switch as shown in Figure 85. Install the 1000 ohm, 1/4-watt, 10% resistor at this time also.

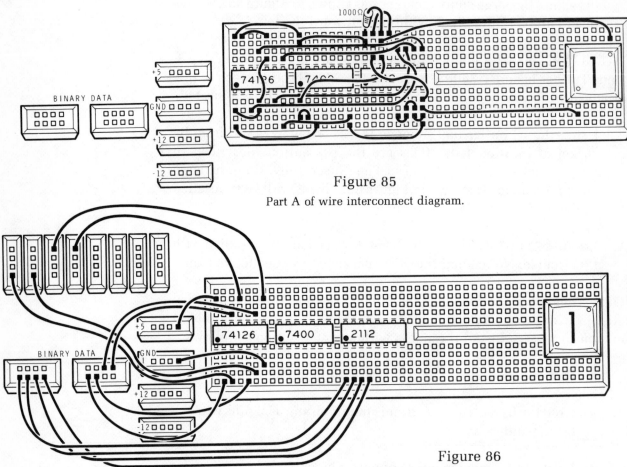

Figure 85

Part A of wire interconnect diagram.

Figure 86

Part B of wire interconnect diagram.

6. Refer to Figure 86 and install hookup wire as shown. Now compare your circuit with the circuit shown in Figure 87. Figures 85 and 86 are supplied to familiarize you with the proper wiring technique. The remaining hardware experiments will show only the circuit diagram.

7. Connect your Trainer line cord plug to a wall receptacle, and switch the circuit power on. The four data LED's may or may not be randomly lit.

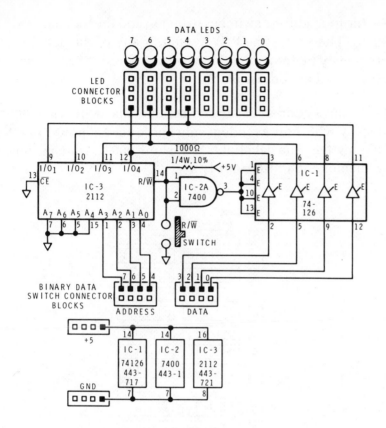

Figure 87
Circuit diagram of the first part of the
memory experiment.

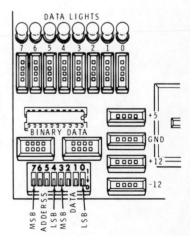

Figure 88
Binary data switch functions.

NOTE: The slide switch assembly in the lower left corner of the Trainer (Figure 88) is used to control address and data information in this experiment. The first four switches (0 thru 3) control data, while the next four (4 thru 7) control the address. Each group is arranged in a binary sequence with the least significant bits at 0 (data) and 4 (address). The physical position of each switch indicates a logic level; up for a logic 1 and down for a logic 0.

The pushbutton switch mounted on the large connector block functions as the memory Read/Write switch. In its out (off) position, the memory is in the read mode, and the four data LED's will display data stored in memory. When the R/W switch is pressed, the memory goes to the write mode, and the value stored in the four data switches is read into memory. The four data LED's immediately display the new memory data.

8. Set the four address switches to 0000_2, and the four data switches to 0000_2. Then press the $R/\overline{W}$ switch. If any of the data LED's were previously lit, they should now be out. This indicates that 0000_2 is now stored at address 0000_2.

9. Now select address 0001_2 and set the data switches to 0001_2. The display will show a random value produced at power-on. Press the $R/\overline{W}$ switch. The data lights will show 0001_2, which is now stored in memory at address 0001_2.

ADDRESS					DATA			
HEX	BINARY				BINARY			
0	0	0	0	0	0	0	0	0
1	0	0	0	1	0	0	0	1
2	0	0	1	0	0	0	1	0
3	0	0	1	1	0	0	1	1
4	0	1	0	0	0	1	0	0
5	0	1	0	1	0	1	0	1
6	0	1	1	0	0	1	1	0
7	0	1	1	1	0	1	1	1
8	1	0	0	0	1	0	0	0
9	1	0	0	1	1	0	0	1
A	1	0	1	0	1	0	1	0
B	1	0	1	1	1	0	1	1
C	1	1	0	0	1	1	0	0
D	1	1	0	1	1	1	0	1
E	1	1	1	0	1	1	1	0
F	1	1	1	1	1	1	1	1

Figure 89

First data table for memory storage experiment.

10. Refer to Figure 89 and use the slide switch assembly to load the remaining 14_{10} address locations (2 thru 15_{10}) with the data specified. NOTE: To write data in memory; select the address, select the data value, and load the data by pressing the $R/\overline{W}$ switch.

11. With the address switches, select memory location 9_{16}. The displayed data is $\_\,\_\,\_\,\_{}_2$. Since the 16 memory locations contain a data value that matches the address, the displayed value should equal 9_{16}. Randomly select various memory locations. As each location is selected, the stored data will be displayed.

ADDRESS		DATA
HEX	BINARY	BINARY
0	0 0 0 0	1 1 1 1
1	0 0 0 1	1 1 1 0
2	0 0 1 0	1 1 0 1
3	0 0 1 1	1 1 0 0
4	0 1 0 0	1 0 1 1
5	0 1 0 1	1 0 1 0
6	0 1 1 0	1 0 0 1
7	0 1 1 1	1 0 0 0
8	1 0 0 0	0 1 1 1
9	1 0 0 1	0 1 1 0
A	1 0 1 0	0 1 0 1
B	1 0 1 1	0 1 0 0
C	1 1 0 0	0 0 1 1
D	1 1 0 1	0 0 1 0
E	1 1 1 0	0 0 0 1
F	1 1 1 1	0 0 0 0

Figure 90

Second data table for memory storage experiment.

12. Refer to Figure 90 and enter the specified data for each address location.

13. Randomly select a number of memory locations and note the stored data. You probably recognized the relationship between address and data while you entered the data. If not, do you now? The data corresponds to the 1's complement of the address. This circuit is being used as a look-up table. By selecting an address, you can retrieve data previously stored away. Similarly, this circuit can be used for code conversion. Using a binary sequence (as in Figures 89 and 90) for addressing, a value code can be stored to represent the address (for example, the Gray code as described in Unit 1). Thus, to find the Gray code value of 8_{16}, simply examine memory location 8_{16}. A second memory circuit can then be used to reconvert the code by using the Gray code values (in this example) for address locations, and the binary values for data.

DISCUSSION

In this section of the experiment, you used a 256 × 4-bit RAM integrated circuit. An IC of this type will have eight address pins and four I/O (input/output) pins through which a 4-bit data word may be stored (written) or read. The direction of I/O flow is determined by the $R/\overline{W}$ (read/write) pin logic level. A logic 1 on this pin defines the four I/O pins as outputs, thus placing the IC in its **read** mode. A logic 0 on the $R/\overline{W}$ pin defines the four I/O pins as inputs, thus placing the IC in its **write** mode. A $\overline{\text{chip enable}}$ ($\overline{CE}$) pin allows the IC to be enabled or disabled without disturbing its memory contents. This feature will be more meaningful in a later experiment.

You also used a 3-state buffer array (four buffers) with the memory circuit. This is necessary to isolate the data switches when the memory is in its read mode. Each buffer acts as an open circuit at its output pin unless a logic 1 is applied to each enable (E) pin. As shown in Figure 87, when the $R/\overline{W}$ switch is pressed, the memory $R/\overline{W}$ line goes low (write mode), and the enable lines to the buffers go high (through NAND gate IC-2A). Switch data is coupled through the buffers and is written into memory. The LED's display the data value. When the $R/\overline{W}$ switch is released, the memory returns to its read mode and the buffers return to their open circuit condition. The LED's now display the data value stored in memory.

Writing into memory requires careful timing. Normally the address and data lines must be stable while the R/$\overline{W}$ line is pulsed low, as shown in Figure 91, part A. Actually, the data is stored as soon as the R/$\overline{W}$ line reaches a logic 0 level. If the data changes value while the R/$\overline{W}$ line is low, the memory will store the new data. In like manner, if the address changes with the R/$\overline{W}$ line low, the same data will be stored at the new address.

Figure 91 part B shows an extreme example of **improper** timing. At address condition 1, data 4 will be stored. Then data 4 will be stored at address 2. However, while at address 2, data changes to condition 5. Therefore, data 5 is now stored at address 2. Finally, data 5 is stored at address condition 3.

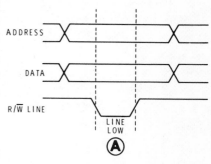

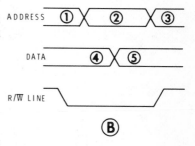

Figure 91

Memory write timing diagram.

Procedure (continued)

14. Turn the Trainer power off, then pull the power plug from the wall receptacle.

NOTE:

If you are using Trainer Model Number ET-3400, perform step 15. For Model Number ET-3400A, perform step 15A. All other steps of this procedure are common to both Trainers, except where indicated.

15. Using the IC puller tool, remove memory IC 2112 (443-721) from its socket at location IC16. (Observe the necessary precautions for handling MOS devices.) Then insert the IC into the large connector block, next to the other memory IC.

15A. Locate the second IC 2112 (#443-721) that was supplied with this course. (Observe the necessary precautions for handling MOS devices.) Then insert the IC into the large connector block, next to the other memory IC.

16A. Using hookup wire, rewire the connector block IC's and Trainer to form the circuit shown in Figure 92. Notice that most of the circuitry is identical to the first circuit you built. You may find it helpful to trace each on the Figure with a red pencil, as you install the wire.

16B. Connect your Trainer line cord plug to a wall receptacle, and switch the circuit power on.

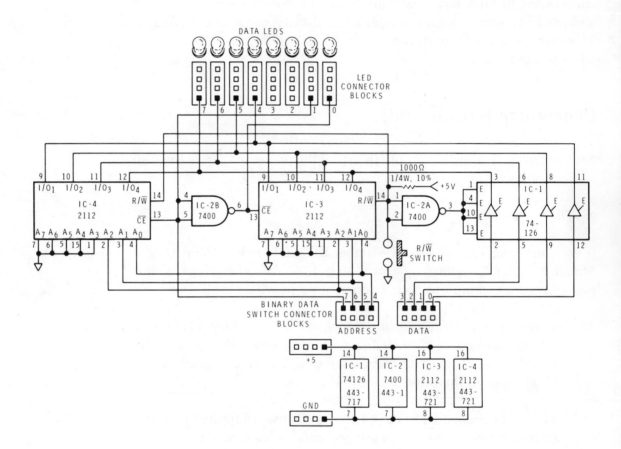

Figure 92

Circuit diagram of the second part of the

memory experiment.

ADDRESS					DATA			
HEX	BINARY				BINARY			
0	0	0	0	0	0	0	0	0
1	0	0	0	1	0	0	0	1
2	0	0	1	0	0	0	1	0
3	0	0	1	1	0	0	1	1
4	0	1	0	0	0	1	0	0
5	0	1	0	1	0	1	0	1
6	0	1	1	0	0	1	1	0
7	0	1	1	1	0	1	1	1
8	1	0	0	0	0	1	1	1
9	1	0	0	1	0	1	1	0
A	1	0	1	0	0	1	0	1
B	1	0	1	1	0	1	0	0
C	1	1	0	0	0	0	1	1
D	1	1	0	1	0	0	1	0
E	1	1	1	0	0	0	0	1
F	1	1	1	1	0	0	0	0

Figure 93

Third data table for memory storage experiment.

17. The address, data, and $R/\overline{W}$ switches function as before. Refer to Figure 93 and enter the data shown, beginning at address 0000_2. NOTE: Data LED0 will be lit for the first eight address locations. Data LED1 will be lit for the last eight address locations.

18. Data LED's 0 and 1 indicate which memory IC is enabled. LED0 lights for IC4 and LED1 lights for IC3. Examine a number of addresses between 0000_2 and 0111_2. Notice which memory IC is enabled. The data stored should match the address. Now examine a number of addresses between 1000_2 and 1111_2. Notice which memory IC is enabled. The data stored should be the 1's complement of the address.

19. Switch the Trainer power off for a few seconds, then switch it back on. Examine a number of memory locations. Have their contents been altered? Do data LED's 0 and 1 still indicate which memory IC is enabled?

DISCUSSION

Refer to Figure 92 and note how data LED's 0 and 1 are connected. They indicate which memory IC is enabled by the MSB address switch. Since IC3 and IC4 share address lines 4, 5, and 6, the chip enable ($\overline{CE}$) pins determine which IC is enabled for data transfer. The most significant address line is connected to pin 13 of IC4 and its complement is connected to pin 13 of IC3. Therefore, when bit 4 (switch 7) of the address is logic 0, IC4 is enabled; and when bit 4 is logic 1, IC3 is enabled.

When either memory IC is disabled, through pin $\overline{CE}$, stored data remains unaffected. The 3-state output pins go to an open circuit condition. This insures that only one memory IC on the common address lines will be active for data transfer.

RAM, unlike ROM, has a volatile memory. Therefore, when power is lost (even momentarily) data stored in memory is no longer valid. However, data can be reentered into memory and retained as long as power remains on.

PROCEDURE (Continued)

20. Switch the Trainer power off.

21. Remove the hookup wires (save them), pushbutton switch, resistor, and IC1 and IC2, used in the previous experiment, from the Trainer.

22. Refer to Figure 94, install the IC's, and wire the circuit to the Trainer. Caution: When you install the IC's, leave an extra set of holes between IC2 and IC3. You will be replacing the 14-pin IC2 with a 16-pin IC at a later time.

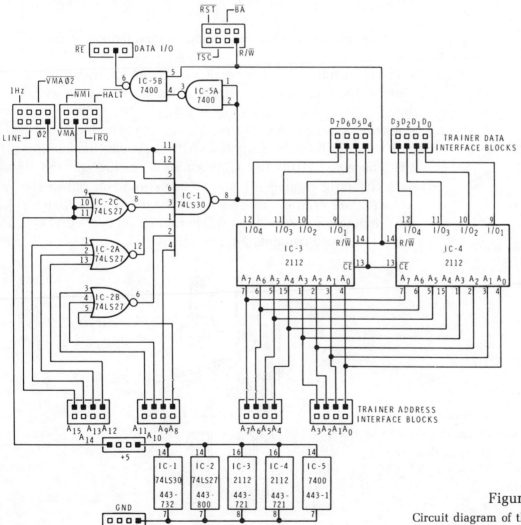

Figure 94

Circuit diagram of the third part of the memory experiment.

23. The memory circuit you have wired now interfaces with the microprocessor and will allow data transfer from address 0200_{16} through $02FF_{16}$. Use the Trainer Examine function and randomly select an address in this memory block. Change the data at this location to AA_{16}. Press the FWD key, then press the BACK key. Is the memory content still AA_{16}?

24. Examine address 0300_{16}. Now change the contents to AA_{16}. Press the FWD key, then press the BACK key. Is the memory content still AA_{16}.

The data you entered in the previous step was retained because of the memory circuit you wired into the Trainer. The data at location 0300_{16} was not retained because no memory exists for that location.

25. Examine address 0200_{16} and change its contents to AA_{16}.

26. Without switching the Trainer power off, interchange the D_6 and D_7 wires at the Data Interface Block, as shown in Figure 95.

27. Press the FWD key, then press the BACK key. The indicated data is now $6A_{16}$. By interchanging the sixth and seventh data bits, $\underline{10}10$ 1010_2 became $\underline{01}10$ 1010_2. The memory IC still retains the orginal data you programmed. To see this relationship, return the two wires to their orginal position. Since the display has "latched in" the previous data, press the FWD key and then the BACK key. The correct memory contents are now displayed.

Figure 95
Physical manipulation of data by interchanging data lines.

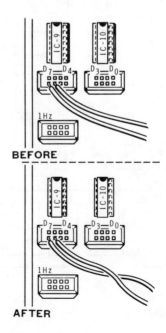

DISCUSSION

IC1 and IC2 shown in Figure 94, form the address decoder. The inputs of this decoder are connected to address lines A_8 thru A_{15}, ϕ_2, and VMA.

To enable the two memory IC's, the $\overline{CE}$ pins must be at logic 0. This will occur when all of the inputs to IC1 are at logic 1. Therefore, only address $0000\ 0010_2$ (02_{16}) will decode properly. This is the high order byte of a 16-bit address. ϕ_2 and VMA will go to a logic 1 sometime during a proper address cycle. When this occurs, the output of IC1 will go to a logic 0, and memory will be enabled.

The low order byte of the 16-bit address determines the memory location in IC3 and IC4 where data will be stored or retrieved. Since each memory IC can store only four bits of data, two IC's are connected in parallel. Thus, 256_{10} 8-bit data words can be stored from address 0200_{16} thru $02FF_{16}$. Therefore, in the circuit shown in Figure 94, address bits A_0 thru A_7 select the memory location and address bits A_8 thru A_{15} select the specific memory IC's to be enabled.

Data flow direction is determined by the $R/\overline{W}$ line. When this line is at logic 0, the MPU can write into memory. When this line is at logic 1, the MPU can read from memory.

In small microprocessor systems (less than ten devices), the MPU and its support IC's can be connected directly together. However, when more circuits are added to the address and data busses, the MPU can no longer supply the necessary current.

To solve this problem, bus extenders (buffers) are connected between the MPU and most of the surrounding IC's. These supply the necessary drive. Figure 96 illustrates a typical circuit.

The address bus extender is uni-directional. That is, it passes a signal in only one direction. It consists of 16 individual buffer drivers; one for each address line.

Unlike address signals, data signals can originate at the MPU or in peripheral circuits such as memory. Therefore, *bi-directional* bus extenders are required. Each data bus extender consists of two 3-state buffer drivers wired back-to-back as shown in Inset 2 of Figure 96. The 3-state feature in this case is complementary. That is, when the read enable ($\overline{\text{RE}}$) control line is low, the read buffer is enabled, and when the $\overline{\text{RE}}$ line is high, the write buffer is enabled. Remember, the terms read and write are always expressed in relation to the MPU.

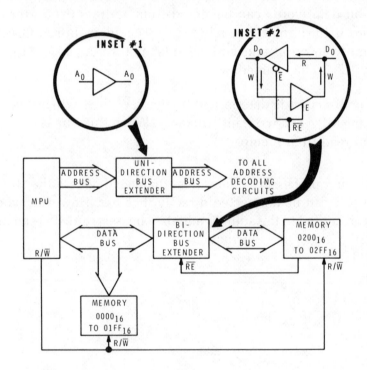

Figure 96

Block diagram of typical microprocessor system using bus extenders.

You may wonder why an $\overline{RE}$ line is required in addition to the R/$\overline{W}$ line. It wouldn't be, if all the memory and any other bus operated devices were electrically connected **outside** of the bus extenders. However, in most systems, there are some circuits connected directly to the MPU, with additional circuits connected to bus extenders. Thus, the $\overline{RE}$ control is necessary for valid logic transfer.

During a read cycle, data is transferred to the MPU from memory or other support devices. When a memory location "down line" from the bus extender is addressed, the bus extender will receive a $\overline{RE}$ logic 0 signal, which enables the buffer in the "read" direction. All devices not addressed, before or after the bus extender, will be 3-stated into their open circuit configuration. In this case, the R/$\overline{W}$ control could have been inverted and connected to the bus extender $\overline{RE}$ input. However, if memory "up line" from the bus extender (MPU side) is addressed, the bus extender must remain in its "write" configuration. It could not do this if the inverted R/$\overline{W}$ control line was used.

Since all of the devices "down line" are 3-stated to their open-circuit condition, the input to the "read" buffer of the bus extender would be undefined and its output would assume a logic level (usually logic 1 for TTL gates) that could interfere with data transfer. By using an $\overline{RE}$ control signal not totally defined by the R/$\overline{W}$ control, the bus extender can be forced into its "write" state and prevent any "down-line" interference.

The circuit you constructed from Figure 94 used the $\overline{CE}$ and R/$\overline{W}$ signals to produce the necessary $\overline{RE}$ signal. This is then used to control the bus extender where it interfaces the data connector blocks with the MPU data bus in the Trainer. As shown in Figure 94, the $\overline{CE}$ signal from pin 8 of IC1 is inverted by IC5A. Thus, when memory IC's 3 and 4 are enabled and the R/$\overline{W}$ line is logic 1, the output of IC5B is logic 0, which enables the bus extender "read" buffer. If IC's 3 and 4 are not enabled, the $\overline{RE}$ line remains high regardless of R/$\overline{W}$ level, and the bus extender remains in its "write" condition.

The final section of this experiment will examine a method for determining the validity of memory. First however, you will learn to read an assembled program listing. This format will be used from now on in these experiments. What you will see is a photocopy of each program as it is assembled and printed by a computer. This serves two purposes: First, it insures that no typographical errors have been introduced during manual reproduction. Second, it gives you an opportunity to become familiar with the format used by most periodicals and books for program listing.

All of the following programs were assembled with a Motorola EXOR-ciser® and printed with a Digital Equipment Corporation Decwriter II®. As shown in Figure 97, each listing can be divided into two main sections. The right half contains the assembly language program just as the programmer typed it into the computer. The left half of the listing was produced (assembled) from the data in the right half of the listing. This half contains the machine language code that must be entered into the Microprocessor Trainer.

The program listing contains eight columns of information. A brief explanation of each follows.

- Column 1 is a sequential list of numbers produced only as a reference to identify listing lines.

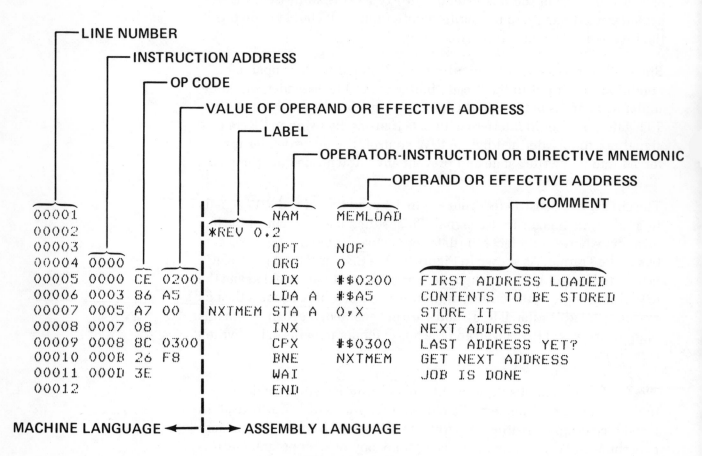

Figure 97
Assembled program for loading data into
a block of memory.

- Column 2 lists each instruction address. Depending on the number of bytes in each instruction, these addresses can be sequential, or spaced 2 or 3 addresses apart. In Figure 97, line 00005 contains instruction address 0000, while line 00006 contains instruction address 0003. This occurred because op code CE required two address bytes 02 and 00 to complete the instruction.

- Column 3 lists instruction op codes only. This accounts for the variable address spacing in column 2.

- Column 4 contains the operand or effective address. Thus, this column may have none, one, or two bytes of data, depending on the op code.

- Column 5 begins the assembly language portion of the program listing. It contains any labels used to assemble the program. If the label is preceded by an asterisk (*), the following information is a comment only, and not used for program assembly. In Figure 97, line 00002 contains the label "*REV 0.2". This is a comment that states this is a program that has been revised two times. It serves only as a handy reference for the programmer to keep track of his program status.

   If the label is not preceded by an asterisk, the label becomes a way of finding an address in a branch or jump routine. Line 00010 contains the instruction BNE followed by NXTMEM. This says, branch if not equal to the address defined by the label NXTMEM. Thus, the program will jump to the address at line 00007, where the label NXTMEM is located.

- Column 6 lists the operator-instruction for the program, or the directive mnemonic used by the assembler.

- Column 7 lists the operand or the effective address of the instruction or directive.

- Column 8 contains any comments the programmer wishes to make. These are usually a description of the program steps to aid in understanding the program.

More information on assembly programming is available in Motorola's "M6800 Microprocessor Applications Manual" (Heath # EDP-244). For the purpose of this section, we will be primarily concerned with machine coding, columns 2, 3, and 4.

PROCEDURE (Continued)

28. Refer to Figure 97 and enter the program beginning at address 0000_{16}.

29. Examine your program beginning at address 0000_{16}. The addresses and their contents should agree with the list in Figure 98.

30. Press RESET, then press DO and enter address 0000_{16}. The display will go dark, indicating the microprocessor is working.

31. Press RESET and examine a number of memory locations between 0200_{16} and $02FF_{16}$. The contents will be $A5_{16}$. You should be able to single-step through each memory location and verify that it functions properly by observing that $A5_{16}$ is stored at each address. By changing the contents at address 0004_{16} to a different value, say $5A_{16}$, and executing the program you can verify that none of the memory defaulted to the original value, $A5_{16}$.

32. This completes the experiment. However, DO NOT disconnect the memory circuit from the Trainer. You will use this circuit in Experiment 13. Proceed to Experiment 12.

ADDRESS	DATA
0000	CE
0001	02
0002	00
0003	86
0004	A5
0005	A7
0006	00
0007	08
0008	8C
0009	03
000A	00
000B	26
000C	F8
000D	3E

Figure 98

Data listing for program in Figure 97.

Experiment 12

Clock

OBJECTIVES:

Show how the interrupt request can be implemented.

Show how an external timing signal can synchronize the MPU.

INTRODUCTION

In this experiment, you will improve the clock program you developed earlier. A line frequency (60 Hz) signal provides timing accuracy to the clock. The line frequency signal is connected to the interrupt request ($\overline{\text{IRQ}}$) input. This makes the clock extremely accurate.

MATERIALS REQUIRED

1   ET-3400 Microprocessor Trainer (with hard-wired circuit).

1   6″ hookup wire.

PROCEDURE

Programming Notes:

- Begin program (listed in Figure 99) at address 0003_{16} (line 00009) and enter data CE_{16}. The first three address locations are reserved for clock display time and will be entered after the main program has been entered.

- As you load the program, notice that no address is specified at lines 00008, 00015, 00023, 00028, 00041, and 00047, and 00052. These lines are used for comments or assembler directives. Just follow the program address sequence and ignore these lines.

- Line 00049 contains an ORG (originate) statement which is an assembler directive. Therefore, you can ignore the address specified. The next instruction you must enter goes to memory location $00F7_{16}$. Use the EXAM and CHAN keys to enter the opcode.

```
00001                              NAM    CLOCK-2  * REV  0.6
00002                        **LINE ACCURACY CLOCK PROGRAM
00003                              OPT    NOP
00004 0000                         ORG    0
00005 0000 0001   SECOND RMB    1
00006 0001 0001   MINUTE RMB    1
00007 0002 0001   HOURS  RMB    1
00008                        ** INTERRUPT HANDLING
00009 0003 CE 003D TIMPAS LDX    #$003D      61
00010 0006 09      ONE60T DEX                TIME TICKING OFF
00011 0007 27 04          BEQ    TIMEUP      60 PULSES YET?
00012 0009 0E             CLI
00013 000A 3E             WAI                WAITING
00014 000B 20 F9          BRA    ONE60T      GO BACK & WAIT AGAIN!
00015                        ** INCR ONE SECOND AND UPDATE
00016 000D C6 60   TIMEUP LDA B  #$60        SIXTY SECONDS,SIXTY MINUTES
00017 000F 0D             SEC                ALWAYS INCREMENT SECONDS
00018 0010 8D 11          BSR    INCR        INCREMENT SECONDS
00019 0012 8D 0F          BSR    INCR        INCREMENT MINUTES IF NEEDED
00020 0014 C6 13          LDA B  #$13        TWELVE HOUR CLOCK
00021 0016 8D 0B          BSR    INCR        INCREMENT HOURS
00022 0018 BD FCBC        JSR    REDIS       RESET DISPLAYS
00023      FCBC   REDIS  EQU    $FCBC
00024 001B 8D 17          BSR    PRINT
00025 001D 8D 15          BSR    PRINT
00026 001F 8D 13          BSR    PRINT       PRINT HOURS,MINUTES,SECONDS
00027 0021 20 E0          BRA    TIMPAS      DO IT ALL AGAIN
00028                        ** INCR - INCREMENT SUBROUTINE
00029 0023 A6 00   INCR   LDA A  0,X         DATA WORD INTO A
00030 0025 89 00          ADC A  #0          INCREMENT IF NECESSARY
00031 0027 19             DAA                FIX TO DECIMAL
00032 0028 11             CBA                TIME TO CLEAR?
00033 0029 25 01          BCS    INC1        NO
00034 002B 4F             CLR A
00035 002C A7 00   INC1   STA A  0,X
00036 002E 08             INX
00037 002F 07             TPA
00038 0030 88 01          EOR A  #1          COMPLEMENT CARRY BIT
00039 0032 06             TAP
00040 0033 39             RTS
00041                        ** PRINT - PRINT HEX BYTES
00042 0034 09      PRINT  DEX                POINT X AT BYTE
00043 0035 96 02          LDA A  $02         WHAT'S IN HOURS?
00044 0037 27 05          BEQ    ADJUST      IF IT'S ZERO
00045 0039 A6 00   CONTIN LDA A  0,X
00046 003B 7E FE20        JMP    OUTBYT
00047      FE20   OUTBYT EQU    $FE20       MONITOR ROUTINE
00048 003E 7C 0002 ADJUST INC    HOURS       MAKE IT ONE
00049 0041 20 F6          BRA    CONTIN      RESUME
00050 00F7                         ORG    $00F7
00051 00F7 3B             RTI
00052                         END
```

Figure 99

Assembled program for real-time clock.

PROCEDURE (Continued)

1. If you have not done so, switch the Trainer on. Then enter the program listed in Figure 99.

2. Refer to Figure 100 and install the 6″ hookup wire between the LINE socket and the $\overline{\text{IRQ}}$ socket. Do not disturb the other circuit you have wired into the Trainer.

3. Your clock is ready to run. Determine at what time you wish to start the clock; then enter the seconds at address 0000_{16}, the minutes at address 0001_{16}, and the hours at address 0002_{16}. For example, to set the clock for 9:25:30, enter the following:

Address	Data	
0000	30	(seconds)
0001	25	(minutes)
0002	09	(hours)

4. Press RESET, then press DO and then enter the first 3 digits of the starting address ($\underline{0}\ \underline{0}\ \underline{0}\ \_{16}$). As the time you have set approaches, enter the fourth digit (3), but do not release the key. At precisely the correct time, release the "3" key. The display will momentarily go dark, and then show the correct time, with the seconds digit updating at a 1-second rate.

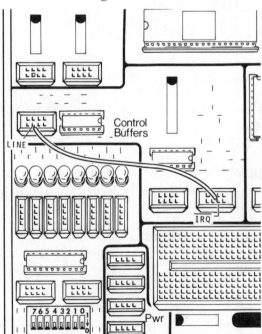

Figure 100

Clock interrupt request line connection.

DISCUSSION

Although it appears to be a simple process to connect the LINE signal to the $\overline{\text{IRQ}}$ input of the microprocessor, AC line voltage had to be reduced in amplitude and processed into a waveform acceptable to the microprocessor. The circuit used by the Trainer is shown in Figure 101. It uses a comparator with positive feedback to process the AC signal.

A sample of AC line signal is coupled through current limiting resistors R1 and R2 to the negative input of the comparator. Diode D1 limits the negative swing of the AC signal to approximately 0.7 volts. The comparator tracks the AC input and switches logic levels at its output, at the same rate. Positive feedback through resistor R6 speeds up the rise and fall times at the output.

A simpler circuit is shown in Figure 101B. Input current is limited by resistor R1, while diodes D1 and D2 limit the voltage swing within TTL levels. As before, the line frequency can be obtained from the secondary of a power transformer. The NAND gate is used to buffer the input signal and provide some speed-up of the rise and fall times.

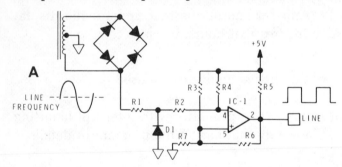

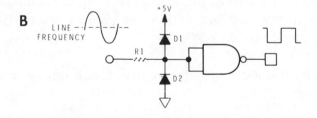

Figure 101
Line frequency signal processing.

If a buffer is already supplied in the system, as in Figure 101C, then it is only necessary to limit the signal current and voltage swing with a resistor and two diodes.

The clock program (Figure 99) is broken down into five main sections. These are:

> Lines 00005-00007. Reserved addresses where the starting seconds, minutes, and hours are stored. As the program progresses, these addresses are updated to current time.

> Lines 00009-00014, and 00051. They handle the interrupt routine, and count the seconds.

> Lines 00016-00027. The main part of the program keeps track of seconds; increments seconds, minutes, and hours when appropriate.

> Lines 00029-00040. A subroutine that handles the mathematical and updating part of the program.

> Lines 00042-00049. Another subroutine that updates the display with new data. Also insures that hours never go to zero.

In addition, a number of monitor subroutines are used.

Since this experiment is concerned primarily with interrupt handling, this discussion will explain only that part of the program in detail.

Line 00009 — Load the index register with the line frequency plus one. (Line frequency is 60_{10}, plus 1 yields 61_{10} or $3D_{16}$.) Thus, when the index register is decremented in the next instruction, the count circuit will provide a precise division by 60.

Line 00010 — Decrement the index register by one. Clock timing has begun.

Line 00011 — The first time through, the index is not zero. Therefore, the branch instruction is not executed. On a later pass, when the index register is zero, the program will branch to TIMEUP.

Line 00013 — Wait for the interrupt request to arrive.

As discussed in Unit 6, when a nonmaskable interrupt ($\overline{\text{NMI}}$) occurs, the contents of the index register, program counter, accumulators, and condition code register are stored in the stack. The program counter is then loaded with a new address that is found at addresses $FFFC_{16}$ and $FFFD_{16}$ (located in ROM). If you examine these addresses, you will find 00_{16} and FD_{16} respectively. The microprocessor will then execute the instruction at address $00FD_{16}$.

Line 00050 — Return from interrupt. When this instruction is executed, the microprocessor retrieves the data previously stored in the stack. This includes the index register and program counter contents. It then executes the instruction pointed to by the program counter.

Line 00013 — Branch always is the instruction immediately following the wait for interrupt. This sends the microprocessor back to line 00010 (ONE6OT).

At this point, you should notice that the program is in a loop that repeats every sixtieth of a second. This will continue until the index register decrements to zero. When zero is attained, the branch-if-zero instruction will send the microprocessor off to the main part of the program, which increments the clock by one second. The interrupt routine repeats again after the clock advances.

The remainder of the program is very similar to the clock program presented earlier. A full explanation of the techniques used was discussed in a previous experiment and is not repeated here.

This completes this experiment. Switch the Trainer power off and remove the wire between LINE and $\overline{\text{IRQ}}$. Do not disturb the remaining wires. The circuit you previously constructed will be used in Experiment 13. Proceed with Experiment 13.

Experiment 13

Address Decoding

OBJECTIVES:

> *Demonstrate the difference between full and partial address decoding.*

> *Show how an address decoding chart is assembled.*

> *Demonstrate how an address can be decoded using various types of logic circuits.*

> *Show how to construct a memory address map.*

INTRODUCTION

Many different combinational logic circuits can be used to decode binary bit patterns. We will examine several decoding techniques in this experiment. The first example will use the circuit you wired in the first experiment.

MATERIALS REQUIRED

1   Microprocessor Trainer (with hard-wired circuit)

1   1000 ohm, 1/4-watt, 10% resistor

1   6″ double-sided foam tape.

1   Large connector block

1   74LS42 integrated circuit (443-807)

1   74LS266 integrated circuit (443-719)

Hookup wire

PROCEDURE

1. Carefully examine the circuit you wired to the Trainer in Experiment 11 to see if any wires have pulled out. Figure 102 is an electrical diagram of the circuit.

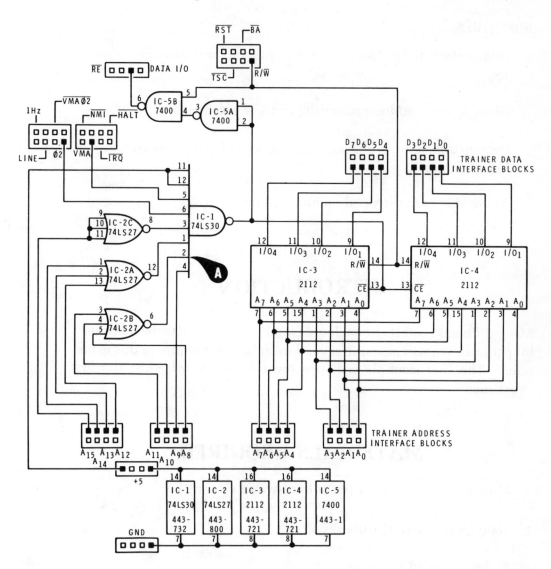

Figure 102

Circuit diagram of the first part of the decoding experiment.

2. Load the program listed in Figure 103 beginning at address 0000_{16} with data CE_{16} and ending at address 0019_{16} with data $E6_{16}$.

3. Press RESET, then press DO and enter 0000_{16}. The display will go out. After approximately three seconds, all display segments and decimal points will light. This is an indication that the program has been executed.

4. You have written BB_{16} into every memory location except where the program resides, and between address 0200_{16} thru $02FF_{16}$. Verify this by examining a number of locations between $001A_{16}$ and $00FF_{16}$. Now examine a number of locations between 0200_{16} and $02FF_{16}$ (hard-wired RAM.)

NOTE: Addresses $00D3_{16}$ thru $00F3_{16}$ will not contain BB_{16}. The Trainer monitor routine uses that portion of RAM.

```
00001                         NAM    DECODECK REV. 0.3
00002                         OPT    NOP
00003  0000 CE 001A  REDO     LDX    #$001A    1ST BLOCK, 1ST ADR
00004  0003 86 BB             LDA A  #$BB      DATA TO BE STORED
00005  0005 A7 00    LOAD1    STA A  X         STORE IT
00006  0007 08                INX              POINT TO NEXT ADR
00007  0008 8C 0200           CPX    #$0200    1ST BLOCK, LAST ADR(+1)
00008  000B 26 F8             BNE    LOAD1
00009  000D CE 0300           LDX    #$0300    2ND BLOCK, FIRST ADR
00010  0010 A7 00    LOAD2    STA A  X         STORE IT
00011  0012 08                INX              POINT TO NEXT ADR
00012  0013 8C 0000           CPX    #0000     2ND BLOCK, LAST ADR(+1)
00013  0016 26 F8             BNE    LOAD2
00014  0018 20 E6             BRA    REDO      RECYCLE
00015                         END
```

Figure 103

Program for memory decoding experiment.

DISCUSSION

The memory you have hard-wired to the Trainer occupies memory space directly above that allocated for "on-board" memory. The assignment is shown in Figure 104. In Experiment 11, you manipulated data within this range. Then you wrote a program to load these addresses (0200_{16} thru $02FF_{16}$) with data. Thus, you found that each space in memory responds to a specific address.

In this experiment, you tried to load data into every possible memory location except the program location and memory block 0200_{16} thru $02FF_{16}$. If your Trainer is an ET-3400, you were unsuccessful with the addresses that do not presently contain RAM. Again, refer to Figure 104A.

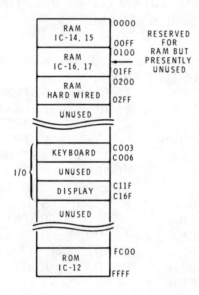

A. ET-3400 MEMORY MAP

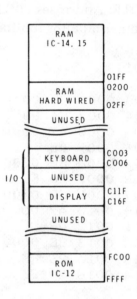

B. ET-3400A MEMORY MAP

Figure 104

Memory map of the Microprocessor
Trainers with additional off-board RAM
at 0200_{16} through $02FF_{16}$.

When addresses 0200_{16} thru $02FF_{16}$ were checked, the contents were not modified by the program. This proves that this section of memory is fully decoded. That is, each location can be accessed with only one specific address.

Although it was described in the Trainer assembly manual, now is a good time to briefly look at the Trainer display. As shown in Figure 104, the display occupies space in the Trainer memory network. In addition, each display segment and decimal point responds to a specific address. Thus, when you entered BB_{16} between 0300_{16} and $FFFF_{16}$ in memory, you also wrote into each display data latch. This is why all of the display segments lit while the program was running.

A decoding chart such as the one shown in Figure 105 can be used to indicate the address code for a memory location. The 1's and 0's in the high byte indicate the logic levels required to enable the memory block, while the X's in the low byte indicate that either a 1 or 0 may be present to select the actual address. Notice that all 16 bits help determine a specific address, which indicates this memory is fully decoded.

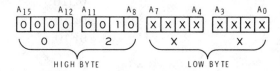

Figure 105

Decoding chart for a memory circuit that
is fully decoding. Includes memory from
0200_{16} to $02FF_{16}$.

PROCEDURE (Continued)

5. Pull the wire end at location A (see Figure 102) from the connector block. Location A is pin 2 of IC1.

6. Now press DO and reexecute the program beginning at address 0000_{16}. Again the display will go out, and then light all segments and decimal points after approximately three seconds.

7. Press RESET and examine a number of addresses between 0200_{16} and $02FF_{16}$. Each address should now contain data BB_{16}.

8. Change the data at address 0210_{16} to AA_{16}.

9. Examine and record the data stored at the following addresses.

0010	_ _	0810	_ _
0110	_ _	0910	_ _
0210	_ _	0A10	_ _
0310	_ _	0B10	_ _
0410	_ _	0C10	_ _
0510	_ _	0D10	_ _
0610	_ _	0E10	_ _
0710	_ _	0F10	_ _

DISCUSSION

When you disconnected IC2B from the circuit, address lines A_8, A_{10}, and A_{11} were no longer able to take part in address decoding. Since line A_9 was still connected, the circuit still decodes to $02XX_{16}$. However, other addresses will now decode the same circuit.

A new decoding chart (see Figure 106) can be assembled by examining the schematic in Figure 102. Bits A_0 thru A_7 are connected directly to memory and select specific addresses in that memory block. An X is placed in each of the corresponding boxes to indicate that the logic levels are unknown but do take part in address selection. Bits A_{12} thru A_{15} must be logic 0 so the correct logic level will be applied to the inputs of NAND gate IC1. Therefore, a 0 is placed in each box.

Disconnecting IC2B removed bits A_8, A_{10}, and A_{11} from the circuit. Since these bits have no effect in the decoding process, these are "don't care" bits. A dot (•) symbol is then placed in each of the corresponding boxes.

Address bit A_9 is still connected to IC1. Since it must be a logic 1 to enable memory, a 1 is placed in its box.

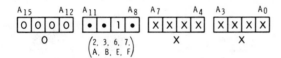

Figure 106

Decoding chart for a memory circuit that is partially decoded. Indicates that many addresses will decode this block of memory.

Once you have constructed a decoding chart, you can determine all of the addresses that will access the circuit. In this case, the most significant four bits are clearly defined as zeroes. The next four bits are more complicated. The only defined bit is A_9. Bits A_8, A_{10}, and A_{11} can be any logic level. Therefore, any hex number which contains the A_9 bit as a logic 1 will be valid. These hex numbers include 2, 3, 6, 7, A, B, E, and F. Bits A_0 through A_7 are variable and select the specific addresses within the circuit.

The chart you completed in step 9 will support this discussion. When you changed the contents of address 0210_{16} to AA_{16}, the addresses that had 3, 6, 7, A, B, E, and F as the second most significant hex digit also appeared to contain AA_{16}. This, of course is impossible, since no memory exists for those addresses.

PROCEDURE (Continued)

10. Switch the Trainer power off. Then carefully remove all of the wires from IC1 and IC2, except for the +5V and ground wires. The remaining circuit wires will remain unchanged in the circuit you are about to construct. To aid you, the new circuit is enclosed by a dashed line in Figure 107.

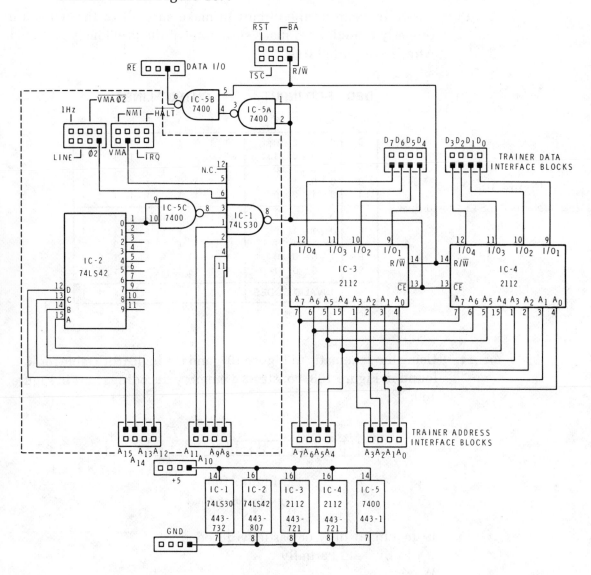

Figure 107

Circuit diagram of the second part of the
memory experiment.

11. Using the IC puller tool, carefully remove IC2 (74LS27). Then install the 74LS42 16-pin IC. Since you are replacing a 14-pin IC with a 16-pin IC, you will have to reposition the +5V wires or ground wires (pin 8 or pin 16).

12. Refer to Figure 107 and wire IC1 and IC2 into the circuit. Note that gate C of IC5 is also wired into the circuit.

13. Carefully examine the circuit to make sure all of the wires are properly routed. Also make sure none of the previously installed wires have pulled free.

DEC	BCD INPUT				OUTPUT LINES									
NO.	D	C	B	A	0	1	2	3	4	5	6	7	8	9
0	0	0	0	0	0	1	1	1	1	1	1	1	1	1
1	0	0	0	1	1	0	1	1	1	1	1	1	1	1
2	0	0	1	0	1	1	0	1	1	1	1	1	1	1
3	0	0	1	1	1	1	1	0	1	1	1	1	1	1
4	0	1	0	0	1	1	1	1	0	1	1	1	1	1
5	0	1	0	1	1	1	1	1	1	0	1	1	1	1
6	0	1	1	0	1	1	1	1	1	1	0	1	1	1
7	0	1	1	1	1	1	1	1	1	1	1	0	1	1
8	1	0	0	0	1	1	1	1	1	1	1	1	0	1
9	1	0	0	1	1	1	1	1	1	1	1	1	1	0
>9	INVALID CODES				1	1	1	1	1	1	1	1	1	1

Figure 108

Logic truth table for 74LS42 4-to-10 line decoder.

14. Using the schematic in Figure 107, and the logic truth table for IC2, found in Figure 108, construct a memory decoding chart in Figure 109.

A_{15} A_{12} A_{11} A_8 A_7 A_4 A_3 A_0

Figure 109

Blank decoding chart.

15. Is the circuit fully or partially decoded?
___ Fully ___ Partially
Why? _____

_____

_____.

16. Now that you have determined the address block your memory resides at, load a few of the addresses with data.

DISCUSSION

The circuit you just constructed contains a fully decoded memory. Its decoding chart is shown in Figure 110. Each bit position is used to define a specific memory address.

In an earlier experiment, you used a combinational logic decoding technique. With that technique, it is necessary to use an individual logic circuit for each memory block. In the circuit you just completed, a 4-to-10 line decoding IC was used to define a block of memory. Since it is possible to define ten different values with four input variables, this device could be used to address ten different memory blocks. Although there was no difference in the number of IC's used in the two experiments, expanding the amount of memory would require fewer device select IC's when the 4-to-10 decoder is used. This can be seen by reexamining the circuits in Figures 102 and 107.

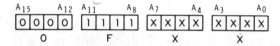

A_{15} A_{12} A_{11} A_8 A_7 A_4 A_3 A_0

| 0 | 0 | 0 | 0 | 1 | 1 | 1 | 1 | X | X | X | X | X | X | X | X |

O   F   X   X

Figure 110
Decoding chart for circuit using 4-to-10
decoding IC.

PROCEDURE (Continued)

17. Switch the Trainer power off. Then disconnect the wire at pin 1 of IC2 (74LS42) and connect it to pin 6 of IC2.

18. The circuit is now fully decoded to address $5FXX_{16}$. This is because every address bit plays a part in determining a specific memory location. Switch the Trainer power on and examine a number of memory locations between $5F00_{16}$ and $5FFF_{16}$. Notice that you can store and read data at these locations. However, you can no longer store and read data at $0F00_{16}$ thru $0FFF_{16}$.

DISCUSSION

The 4-to-10 line decoder can also be used to quickly change decoding addresses, as you have just done. Keep in mind that this experiment uses only one 4-to-10 line decoder to define the most significant hex number. It is not unusual to see them used at lower order addresses. Your Microprocessor Trainer uses this decoding technique for its "on-board" memory.

PROCEDURE (Continued)

19. At this time, you will need more breadboarding space. Locate the box containing the large connector block. Then refer to part A of Figure 111 and install the connector strips supplied with the block. You may have some strips left over.

20. Refer to Figure 111B. Then remove the paper backing from the vinyl strip supplied with the block, line up the long edges of the strip and block, and press the sticky side of the vinyl strip against the block.

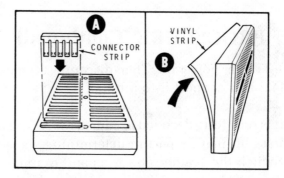

Figure 111
Large connector block assembly.

21. Read this whole step, then locate the foam tape and cut two 3/4″ squares from it. Refer to Figure 112. Remove the paper backing from one side of each square and affix each square to the small edge of the Trainer cabinet as shown. The spacing between the squares should be a little less than the length of the connector block. Now remove the paper backing from the other side of the squares and affix the connector block to the squares. Try to center the squares on the back of the block. This block will provide additional breadboarding space.

22. Switch the Trainer power off and install a 74LS266 (443-719) IC in the new large connector block, near the left end. This IC will become IC6 in the circuit you construct next.

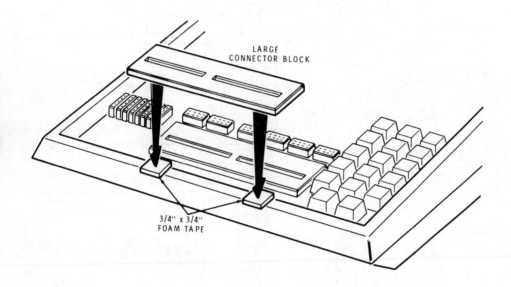

Figure 112
Outboard connector block installation.

23. Connect +5-volt power to pin 14 and ground to pin 7. Then refer to Figure 113 and construct the circuit shown. To aid you, the area enclosed by the dashed line is the only area where modifications are made to the previous circuit.

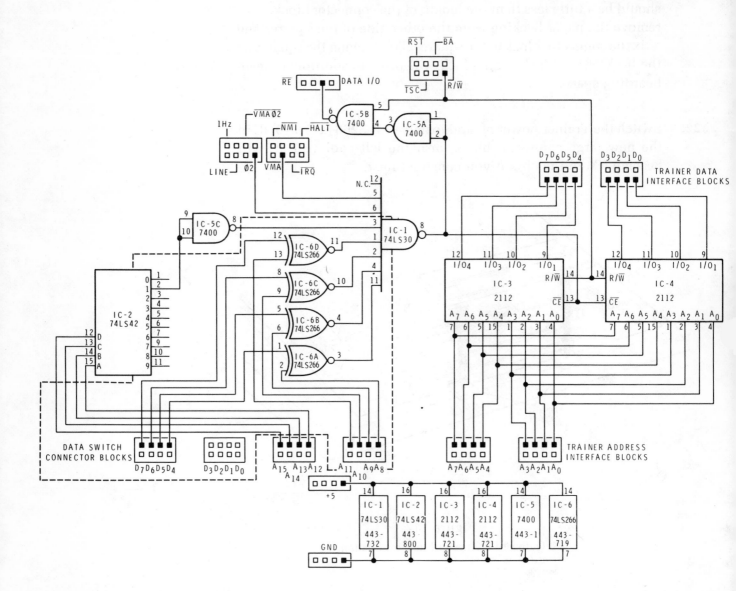

Figure 113

Circuit diagram of the third part of the
decoding experiment.

24. Recheck the wiring to insure it is correct. Be sure pins 9 and 10 of IC5C are connected to pin 2 of IC2.

25. Refer to Figure 114. This is the truth table for a gate in IC6. Notice that if the B input is held at logic 0, the relationship between input A and output Y is complementary (A is the inverse of Y). If the B input is held at a logic 1, the relationship between A and Y is direct (no inversion). Thus, input B can be used as a direct driver or an inverter driver. This feature will be used in the experiment.

$$A \oplus B = Y$$

A	B	Y
0	0	1
1	0	0
0	1	0
1	1	1

Figure 114
Truth table for exclusive NOR (ENOR) gate.

26. Position all of the data switches in the down (logic 0) position.

27. Using the schematic in Figure 113 and the table in Figure 114, determine the decoding chart for the circuit you constructed. Fill in the blank decoding chart in Figure 115.

28. Is the address fully or partially decoded?
    Fully ___ Partially ___

29. What is the address block this circuit will decode?
    $- - - -_{16}$ thru $- - - -_{16}$

30. Switch the Trainer on. Then enter data into a number of addresses in the address block you calculated.

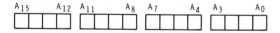

Figure 115
Blank decoding chart.

DISCUSSION

The exclusive NOR gates used in the circuit all function as inverter drivers. Since each is connected to an individual input in IC1, and the 4-to-10 line decoder is still in the circuit, each address line plays a part in determining a specific address. Therefore, this circuit is fully decoded, and occupies addresses 1000_{16} thru $10FF_{16}$.

PROCEDURE (Continued)

31. Change data switches D_7 through D_4 to 0101_2. This equals hex 5.

32. What is the address block this circuit will now decode? $\_\,\_\,\_\,\_{}_{16}$ thru $\_\,\_\,\_\,\_{}_{16}$

33. Test the new address to see if the circuit will respond properly.

DISCUSSION

Now you see the power of the exclusive NOR gate. Addresses are easily switched through them. Notice that whatever binary bit pattern you select with the data switch, the circuit responds to it. Now you will see one other feature of these particular exclusive NOR gates.

PROCEDURE (Continued)

34. Switch the Trainer power off. Refer to Figure 113. Remove the three wires interconnecting IC1 and IC6, from pin 11 to pin 3, pin 4 to pin 4, and pin 2 to pin 10. Refer to Figure 116. Then interconnect pins 3, 4, 10, and 11 of IC6. Finally, insert a 1000 ohm, 1/4-watt, 10% resistor between +5 volts and IC6, pin 11.

35. The circuit should still be located at address block 1500_{16} thru $15FF_{16}$. Check a few of the addresses where you previously entered data. They should contain the same data.

36. Change the data switches to a new bit pattern, determine the address code, then examine a few locations to assure yourself of address code accuracy. Repeat this procedure a number of times.

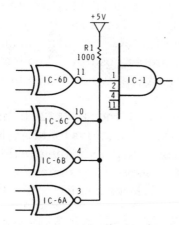

Figure 116
Modification to third circuit of experiment.

REVIEW

The 74LS266 exclusive NOR gate has a special characteristic; it has an open-collector output. This means that a number of gates can be tied together, as you just did. The electrical term for this procedure is wire-OR'ing, where the outputs function as though they were inputs to an OR gate.

One more aspect of circuit decoding will be discussed before the next experiment. This is important, since an experimental error could possibly result in the destruction of a gate or memory package.

A problem arises when two circuits decode to the same address. If two memories containing different data occupy the same address, they will try to pull the data lines in two different directions. Since this is electrically impossible, one circuit will give in, usually resulting in permanent destruction to the circuit. Thus, it is important when designing circuits like those used in this experiment to always check for conflicts in address decoding.

PROCEDURE (Continued)

37.   Switch the Trainer power off and pull the line cord plug.

38.   Pull the hookup wires from the circuit and save them for future use.

NOTE: If your Trainer is an ET-3400, perform step 39. If your Trainer is an ET-3400A, perform step 39A.

39.   Carefully remove IC's 3 and 4 (2112) from the large connector block and install them in IC sockets 16 and 17 in the Trainer. Observe the normal precautions for MOS devices, and make sure you align pin 1 of each IC to the proper position. Then remove all of the remaining components from the two large connector blocks.

39A.   Carefully remove IC's 3 and 4 (2112) from the large connector block. Observing the precautions for MOS devices, place them on the anti-static pad prior to placing them in the small parts container furnished with this course. Then remove all of the remaining components from the two large connector blocks.

DISCUSSION

Your Microprocessor Trainer now contains 512_{10} bytes of RAM. This is located at addresses 0000_{16} through $01FF_{16}$. Proceed to Experiment 14.

Experiment 14

Data Output

OBJECTIVES:

> *Demonstrate microprocessor interfacing to an external data display.*
>
> *Show how a 7-segment display is connected.*
>
> *Demonstrate the trade-offs between hardware and software display decoding.*
>
> *Provide an opportunity to write a number of output programs.*

INTRODUCTION

Until now, you have been using programs that moved data within the Trainer, with any results displayed by the "on-board" LED's. This may be adequate for your purposes, but other methods are needed if external equipment uses the data. The data may take the form of a visual display for an operator to read, or a digital control signal to manipulate an electro-mechanical device. This experiment will present a number of interfacing methods and examine some of the advantages and disadvantages of each method.

MATERIAL REQUIRED

1   ET-3400 Microprocessor Trainer

8   470 ohm, 1/4-watt, 5% resistors

2   10 k ohm, 1/2-watt, 5% resistors

1   FND-500 7-segment LED (411-819)

1   TIL-312 7-segment LED (411-831)

1   7400 integrated circuit (443-1)

2   7475 integrated circuits (443-13)

1   9368 integrated circuit (443-694)

1   74LS30 integrated circuit (443-732)

1   74LS27 integrated circuit (443-800)

1   74LS259 integrated circuit (443-804)

Hookup wire

PROCEDURE

1. In this part of the experiment, you will examine how the MPU can be interfaced to LED's. Make sure the Trainer power is switched off; then construct the circuit shown in Figure 117. Notice that +5 volts and ground are connected to pins 5 and 12 respectively for IC's 1 and 2 (7475). The other IC's use pin 14 for +5 volts and pin 7 for ground.

2. Recheck your wiring; then switch the Trainer power on. The data LED's will show a random value.

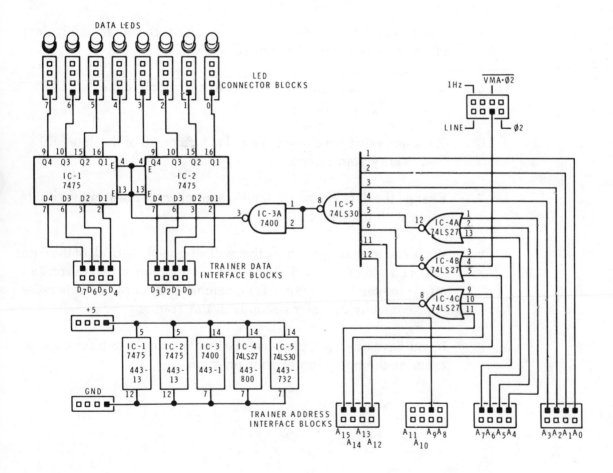

Figure 117
Circuit diagram of the first part of the
output experiment.

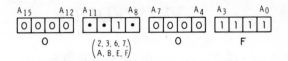

Figure 118

Decoding chart for outputting information to the data LED's.

3.   Figure 118 is a decoding chart for the circuit you constructed. This
shows that the circuit is partially decoded. A 2-digit hex number
can be stored at any of these decoded addresses. Examine address
$020F_{16}$. Then change the contents to 55_{16}.

4.   The data LED's indicate $_____{}_2$. This is the binary equivalent
of the data you stored at address $020F_{16}$.

5.   What hex value would be required to turn off all of the data LED's?
$\_\_{}_{16}$. Verify your answer.

6.   What hex value would be required to turn on all of the data LED's?
$\_\_{}_{16}$. Verify your answer.

7.   Change the data at address $020F_{16}$ a number of times and verify its
value with the data LED's.

8.   Write and execute a program that will alternately turn all of the data
LED's on and off. Use a delay loop in the program so that the on and
off cycles can be recognized. Remember that an MPU cycle takes
approximately 2.5 microseconds in the Trainer.

   If you have any difficulty, use the Trainer single-step function to
examine the operation of your program.

DISCUSSION

Refer to Figures 117 and 118. Notice that a partial decoding scheme is used. A fully decoded circuit could have been used by adding more combinational logic.

In previous decoding circuits, the VMA and $\phi2$ signals were separate. A logic 1 indicated their true state. In this experiment, we took advantage of another Trainer output; the $\overline{VMA \cdot \phi2}$ line. It is logic 0 when both the VMA and $\phi2$ signals are at their true state. This reduces the number of logic gates needed for decoding.

The circuit you constructed appears as a **write only memory** to the microprocessor. That is, the MPU can write into the selected address, but it can not read the data stored. However, since eight data LED's monitor the stored information, you can **read** the data. Thus, the MPU is interfaced in a way that produces usable data.

Two bistable quad latch IC's are enabled when one of the eight pre-selected addresses is accessed. They act as an 8-bit memory storage device. Thus, any data appearing on the data lines is latched into the two devices. Since the output of each latch is active, the data LED connected to each will follow the data level. Storing 00_{16} will turn off all of the LED's, while storing FF_{16} will turn each LED on.

Right now, the data LED's should be switching on and off at a regular interval, because of the program you wrote and executed. If you had any difficulty with the program, refer to Figure 119. It lists a program to flash the data LED's. While this program may not match your program, it is one of many ways to accomplish the same objective.

```
00001                        NAM      FLASHER1 REV. 0.1
00002                        OPT      NOP
00003 0000 4F                CLR A             ACC NOW 0
00004 0001 B7 020F  ALTER    STA A    $020F    STORE ACC TO LIGHTS
00005 0004 CE 5500           LDX      #$5500   *
00006 0007 09       WAIT     DEX               *WAIT
00007 0008 26 FD             BNE      WAIT     *
00008 000A 43                COM A             TOGGLE ACC
00009 000B 20 F4             BRA      ALTER    GO BACK TO RESTORE
00010                        END
```

Figure 119
Program to flash data LED's at regular intervals.

PROCEDURE (Continued)

9. Write a program to alternately store 1's and 0's to the display LED's. But this time, adjust the timing so the LED "on" time is longer than the "off" time. Then execute the program.

DISCUSSION

This program required two timing loops, to allow for the difference between on and off time. If your first program contained two timing loops of equal duration, it was a simple matter to modify the delay times. Figure 120 illustrates a second method for accomplishing the task.

In the next part of the experiment, you will add a decoder-driver and a common cathode, 7-segment display to the circuit.

```
00001                          NAM     FLASHER2 REV. 0.1
00002                          OPT     NOP
00003 0000                     ORG     0
00004 0000 4F             CLR A              ACC NOW "0"
00005 0001 CE 5500 CYCLE  LDX     #$5500     LOGIC "0" TIME
00006 0004 B7 020F        STA A   $020F
00007 0007 43             COM A              BITS NOW "1"
00008 0008 09       HOLD1  DEX
00009 0009 26 FD          BNE     HOLD1
00010 000B CE FF00        LDX     #$FF00     LOGIC "1" TIME
00011 000E B7 020F        STA A   $020F
00012 0011 43             COM A              BITS NOW "0"
00013 0012 09       HOLD2  DEX
00014 0013 26 FD          BNE     HOLD2
00015 0015 20 EA          BRA     CYCLE      ONE CYCLE COMPLETE
00016                          END
```

Figure 120
Program to flash data LED's at a nonregu-
lar interval, with the on time longer than
off time.

PROCEDURE (Continued)

10. Switch the Trainer power off. Then, without disturbing the circuit wired to the Trainer, add the circuit shown in Figure 121. Use the large connector block affixed to the Trainer cabinet to hold the new circuit. The FND-500 (#411-819) display is the larger of the two displays.

11. Recheck your wiring, then switch the Trainer power on, and press RESET.

12. The lower four bits of your data byte will determine the digit displayed. Enter $A5_{16}$ into address $020F_{16}$.

13. What is the bit pattern displayed by the lower four display LED's? $\_\ \_\ \_\ \_{}_2$.

14. What is the hex equivalent? $\_{}_{16}$.

15. What is displayed by the new 7-segment display? $\_{}_{16}$.

16. Write a program that will cause the 7-segment display to count from 0 to F_{16} and then continuously repeat. Include a delay loop so that each digit will remain on long enough to be identified. Execute the program.

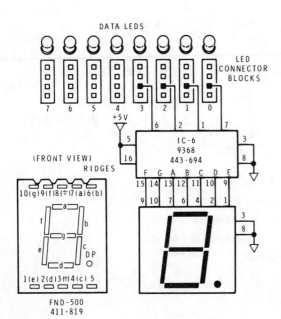

Figure 121

Additional data display for first output circuit.

DISCUSSION

The circuit you just constructed contains a 4-line-to-7-segment decoder driver and a 7-segment, common cathode display. The decoder driver (9368) contains a large maze of combinational logic which allows it to decode four data bits and drive the proper segments in a 7-segment display to produce the corresponding hex digit.

The display circuit is a multiple LED array with common cathodes. The cathodes are grounded, and the decoder driver supplies the necessary power (approximately 30 mA at +5 volts) to light the selected LED segments.

If you had any questions concerning the program to increment the display, refer to Figure 122. It contains a simple program to increment the display from 0 to F_{16} at a slow rate. The simplicity of this program assignment removes the need to reset accumulator A after incrementing to $0F_{16}$. It continues beyond $0F_{16}$. But, since only the four lower bits of data are decoded, it appears to count to $0F_{16}$ and then reset to 00_{16}. Enter the program in Figure 122 and watch the eight data LED's. They show the actual value stored in accumulator A.

Next you will see how the MPU handles common-anode type displays. Also, you will see that a decoder driver is not necessary if you are willing to let the MPU do the decoding.

```
00001                          NAM     STEP-UP    REV.0.4
00002                          OPT     NOP
00003 0000 4F                  CLR A              START WITH 0
00004 0001 B7 020F  UPDATE     STA A   $020F      STORE TO OUTPUT
00005 0004 4C                  INC A              ADD ONE
00006 0005 CE FFFF             LDX     #$FFFF     TIME TO WAIT
00007 0008 09       UPDAT2     DEX                TIME RUNNING OUT
00008 0009 26 FD               BNE     UPDAT2     TIME UP YET?
00009 000B 20 F4               BRA     UPDATE
00010                          END
```

Figure 122

Program to increment the 7-segment display from 0 to F_{16} in an apparent cyclic manner.

PROCEDURE (Continued)

17. Switch Trainer power off and remove the wires, decoder driver, and display package from the large connector block affixed to the Trainer cabinet.

18. Refer to Figure 123 and construct the circuit shown. Since the resistor leads are too short to reach from the connector block to the data LED connectors, insert the free end of each resistor into an unused connector socket. Then run hookup wire to the appropriate LED connector block.

19. Reexamine the circuit to make sure it is properly wired, and the resistor leads do not touch adjacent resistor leads. Then switch Trainer power on and press RESET.

20. This circuit, like the previous circuit, uses the address decoder and latches initially wired to the Trainer. Data stored at address $020F_{16}$ will determine which display segment will light. Enter 00_{16} at address $020F_{16}$. What does the display indicate? $\_\_{16}$.

21. Change the data to FF_{16}. What does the display indicate? $\_\_{16}$.

22. To light a particular segment in the display, the corresponding data bit must be logic 0. The table below the circuit in Figure 123 indicates the segments connected to the data bits. What bit pattern will produce the number 1 in the display? $_____{2}$.

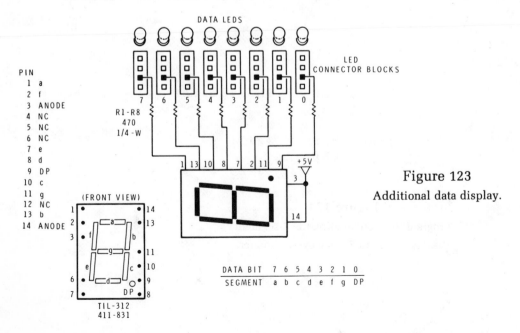

Figure 123
Additional data display.

DATA BIT	7	6	5	4	3	2	1	0
SEGMENT	a	b	c	d	e	f	g	DP

23. Convert the bit pattern from step 22 to hex and enter it at address 020F$_{16}$. Although it is possible to display two 1's, the correct 1 is produced when segments b and c are lit.

24. Load and execute the program shown in Figure 124.

```
00001                          NAM     CHAROUT1 REV. 0.1
00002                          OPT     NOP
00003        020F     DISPLA   EQU     $020F
00004 0000                     ORG     0
00005 0000 CE 001A   RECYCL    LDX     #CODES       START OF TABLE
00006 0003 A6 00     NXTDIG    LDA  A  X            LOAD BIT PATTERN
00007 0005 B7 020F             STA  A  DISPLA       STORE TO DISPLA
00008 0008 86 FF               LDA  A  #$FF         *
00009 000A C6 55     HOLD1     LDA  B  #$55         *
00010 000C 5A        HOLD2     DEC  B               * WAIT
00011 000D 26 FD               BNE     HOLD2        *
00012 000F 4A                  DEC  A               *
00013 0010 26 F8               BNE     HOLD1        *
00014 0012 08                  INX                  POINT TO NXT PATTERN
00015 0013 8C 002A             CPX     #FINAL+1 LAST ONE YET?
00016 0016 27 E8               BEQ     RECYCL       IF SO, START AGAIN
00017 0018 20 E9               BRA     NXTDIG       IF NOT, NXT PATTERN
00018 001A 03        CODES     FCB     $03,$9F,$25,$0D,$99,$49
      001B 9F
      001C 25
      001D 0D
      001E 99
      001F 49
00019 0020 41                  FCB     $41,$1F,$01,$19,$11,$C0
      0021 1F
      0022 01
      0023 19
      0024 11
      0025 C0
00020 0026 63                  FCB     $63,$85,$61
      0027 85
      0028 61
00021 0029 71        FINAL     FCB     $71
00022                          END
```

Figure 124
Program for incrementing the 7-segment
display from 0 to F$_{16}$ in a cyclic manner.

DISCUSSION

In this experiment, you have successfully eliminated a decoder driver, but at the expense of increased software. The program sequentially stores bit patterns to the display to make it appear as number 0 thru F_{16} are being stored.

Addresses $001A_{16}$ thru 0029_{16} contain the sixteen display codes in numerical sequence. This "look-up" table is then accessed by the index register to obtain the required code.

You may have noticed that the B_{16} digit had a decimal point lit next to it. This is sometimes used to indicate it is a B rather than a 6. If you prefer not to have the decimal point, you can change address 0025_{16} to $C1_{16}$.

The display used in this circuit is of the common anode type, with the anodes connected to +5 volts. To turn on a segment, its cathode must be grounded. Therefore, a logic 0 turns on a segment while a logic 1 turns it off.

In some applications, it is convenient to assign each segment of the display its own address. In the next part of the experiment, you will see how this is accomplished.

PROCEDURE (Continued)

25. Switch the Trainer power off. Then remove all of the wires and components from both large connector blocks.

26. Refer to Figure 125 and construct this circuit on the Trainer's large connector block.

27. Switch the Trainer power on. Then enter 00_{16} at address $02F0_{16}$. Since only the D_0 bit is connected to the display circuit, a logic 0 will turn a display segment on, and a logic 1 will turn the segment off.

28. Advance the address and enter 00_{16}. Continue this process and observe the display. Stop after you enter 00_{16} at $02F7_{16}$. Notice that all of the display segments are lit, including the decimal point.

29. Examine address $02F0_{16}$ and watch the display. Now advance through the next seven address locations while you watch the display. What is finally displayed? _____. Why? _____

_____

_____.

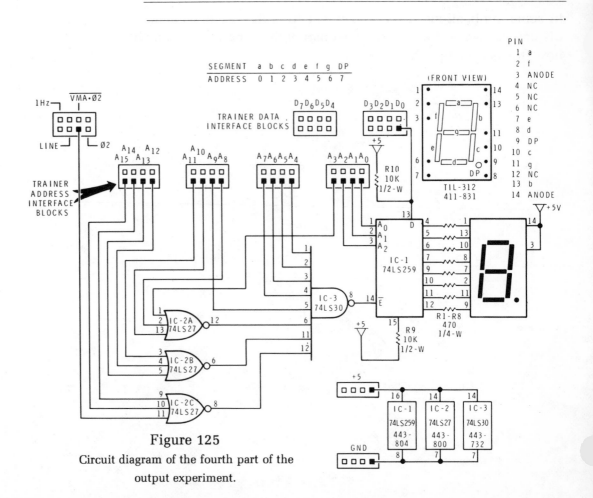

Figure 125

Circuit diagram of the fourth part of the output experiment.

DISCUSSION

Each display segment now has its own address in memory. This is shown in the circuit decoding chart in Figure 126. Refer to Figure 125. Address bits A_0, A_1, and A_2 are decoded to select 1-of-8 bistable latches in IC1. Then during an MPU write operation, the logic information supplied by data bit D_0 is coupled into the selected latch. A logic 0 will turn on the appropriate display segment, while a logic 1 will turn off the segment. A table showing address/segment data is provided in Figure 125, above the circuit diagram. The remaining address bits, and $\overline{VMA \cdot \phi 2}$ are used to enable ($\overline{E}$) the latches.

Since this circuit is the write-only type, the D_0 line will "float" during an MPU read operation. Therefore, the D input of IC1 will go high (10 k ohm pull-up to +5 volts) and couple a logic 1 into the latch. This is why a segment went out when you examined its address without entering data.

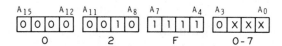

Figure 126
Decoding chart for the fourth output circuit.

PROCEDURE (Continued)

30. Load the program listed in Figure 127. Begin at address 0001_{16}. (Address 0000_{16} is reserved for data.) Notice that the comment column in step 0013_{10} indicates this program will be used as a subroutine in a future program.

```
00001                          NAM    CHAROUT2 REV. 0.2
00002                          OPT    NOP
00003 0000                     ORG    0
00004      02F0    SEGMEN EQU   $02F0
00005 0000 0001    CHARAC RMB   1
00006 0001 CE 02F7 OUTCHR LDX   #SEGMEN+7  TOP OF SEG. LIST
00007 0004 D6 00           LDA B CHARAC     GET PATTERN
00008 0006 E7 00    NXTSEG STA B 0,X        STORE TO LATCH
00009 0008 56              ROR B            SHFT FOR NXT BIT
00010 0009 09              DEX
00011 000A 8C 02EF         CPX   #SEGMEN-1  LAST SEG. YET?
00012 000D 26 F7           BNE   NXTSEG
00013 000F 3E              WAI              DONE(39 FOR SUBROUTINE)
00014                      END
```

Figure 127

Program for writing data into a 7-segment
display.

31. Refer to the display data table in Figure 128 and select a hex digit. Then enter the corresponding data at address 0000_{16}.

32. Execute the program beginning at address 0001_{16}. The hex digit you selected will appear in the 7-segment display.

DIGIT	DATA
0	03
1	9F
2	25
3	0D
4	99
5	49
6	41
7	1F
8	01
9	19
A	11
B	C0
C	63
D	85
E	61
F	71

Figure 128

Display data table for the character output
program.

33. Load the program listed in Figure 129. Begin at address 0102_{16} (step 00006_{10}). (Addresses 0100 and 0101_{16} are reserved for data.) Then enter 39_{16} at address $000F_{16}$. The program located at addresses 0001 thru $000F_{16}$ is a subroutine for the program you just entered. The data stored at addresses 0124 thru 0133_{16} serve as a look-up table for the 16 hex digits you will display.

34. Execute the program beginning at address 0102_{16}. The 7-segment display will sequentially show the hex digits 0 thru F in a cyclic manner.

```
00001                              NAM     OUTSTRIG REV. 0.3
00002 0100                         ORG     $0100
00003       0000    CHARAC  EQU    00
00004 0100  0002    ISAVE   RMB    2
00005       0001    OUTCHR  EQU    01
00006 0102  CE 0124 START   LDX    #CODES      POINT TO CODE TBL
00007 0105  A6 00   NXTDIG  LDA A  0,X         GET PATTERN
00008 0107  97 00           STA A  CHARAC      STORE IT
00009 0109  FF 0100         STX    ISAVE       SAVE INDEX
00010 010C  BD 0001         JSR    OUTCHR      OUTPUT DIGIT
00011 010F  FE 0100         LDX    ISAVE       RESTORE INDEX
00012 0112  86 FF           LDA A  #$FF        *
00013 0114  C6 55   HOLD1   LDA B  #$55        *
00014 0116  5A      HOLD2   DEC B              *
00015 0117  26 FD           BNE    HOLD2       * WAIT
00016 0119  4A              DEC A              *
00017 011A  26 F8           BNE    HOLD1       *
00018 011C  08              INX                POINT TO NXT CODE
00019 011D  8C 0134         CPX    #FINAL+1
00020 0120  27 E0           BEQ    START       RECYCLE
00021 0122  20 E1           BRA    NXTDIG      GET NXT DIGIT
00022 0124  03      CODES   FCB    $03,$9F,$25,$0D,$99
      0125  9F
      0126  25
      0127  0D
      0128  99
00023 0129  49              FCB    $49,$41,$1F,$01,$19
      012A  41
      012B  1F
      012C  01
      012D  19
00024 012E  11              FCB    $11,$C0,$63,$85,$61
      012F  C0
      0130  63
      0131  85
      0132  61
00025 0133  71      FINAL   FCB    $71
00026                       END
```

Figure 129

Program for outputting hex digits in
sequence and in a cyclic manner. Requires program from Figure 127 as a subroutine.

DISCUSSION

With each reduction in hardware, there is generally an increase in support software. The program in Figure 127 is used only to output the necessary data bits to produce a single hex character. Since eight separate address locations are needed to light the 7-digit segments and the decimal point, the program must output eight bytes of data in order to produce the desired display. This is accomplished by using the index register to monitor each segment address and outputting the appropriate data from the B accumulator.

Remember that only the D_0 data bit is connected to the display latch. Thus, you can enter the appropriate 8-bit word (for the hex digit) into the B accumulator and then write the word to the display, which only accepts the D_0 bit. After the word is written, the B accumulator is rotated right, which places the next most significant data bit (for the hex digit) at the D_0 position. The index register decrements to the next segment address and the program branches back to the store B accumulator step. This process continues until all of the display latches are filled, then the branch step defaults and the MPU goes into a wait for interrupt condition. The second program you entered is similar to the previous cyclic character output programs. At step 00010_{10}, a jump to subroutine instruction sends the MPU back to the character output subroutine.

PROCEDURE (Continued)

35. Switch the Trainer power off. Then remove the hookup wire and the components from the large connector block.

36. This completes this experiment.

Experiment 15

Data Input

OBJECTIVES:

> *Show how to construct a circuit for writing data to the microprocessor.*

> *Demonstrate various methods for programming the microprocessor to accept externally applied data.*

> *Demonstrate a software routine for debouncing a switch.*

> *Show how to select a debounce routine to fit a specific system.*

INTRODUCTION

Experiment 14 introduced you to various methods of outputting data from the microprocessor. In this experiment, you will learn how to input data. While many devices can be used to transfer data to a microprocessor (teletypewriter, tape reader, modem, transducer, etc.), they all accomplish their task in basically the same manner. You will use the Trainer binary data switches and four external pushbutton switches for data entry.

MATERIALS REQUIRED

1   ET-3400 Microprocessor Trainer

1   #1 switch

1   #2 switch

1   #3 switch

1   #4 switch

1   7400 integrated circuit (443-1)

1   74126 integrated circuit (443-717)

2   74LS30 integrated circuits (443-732)

1   74LS27 integrated circuit (443-800)

Hookup wire

PROCEDURE

1. In the first part of this experiment, you will interface four slide switches to the data bus of the MPU. Make sure the Trainer power is switched off. Then construct the circuit shown in Figure 130.

2. Make sure all of the binary data switches are down (logic 0). Then position switch 0 up to logic 1.

NOTE: You may have noticed that the display is faintly illuminated with Trainer power off. This is caused by current from the data lines being coupled through IC1 to the +5-volt connector block, and from there to the displays. Disregard the display with power off.

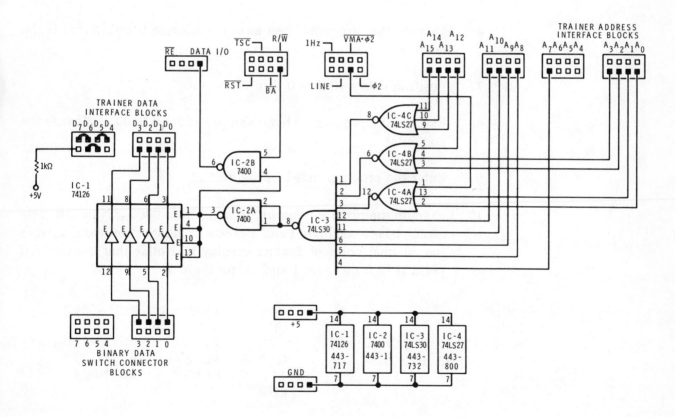

Figure 130
Circuit diagram of the first part of the
input experiment.

3. Switch Trainer power on and enter the program listed in Figure 131. Then execute the program beginning at address 0000_{16}.

```
00001                              NAM    INPUT-01 REV. 0.2
00002                              OPT    NOP
00003 0000 B6 OF80                 LDA A  $0F80      GET DATA
00004 0003 B7 0100                 STA A  $0100      SAVE IT
00005 0006 3E                      WAI               DONE
00006                              END
```

Figure 131
Program for inputting data from the binary data switches.

4. Examine address 0100_{16}. What is the contents? $\_\_{}_{16}$.

5. Position data switch 0 down to logic 0. Then position data switch 1 up to logic 1.

6. Execute the program. Then examine address 0100_{16}. What is the contents? $\_\_{}_{16}$.

7. Position data switches 0 thru 3 up to logic 1.

8. Execute the program. Then examine address 0100_{16}. What is the contents? $\_\_{}_{16}$.

9. Enter the program listed in Figure 132.

10. Execute the program beginning at address 0000_{16}. Now flip data switch 0 between logic 1 and logic 0 a number of times and observe the decimal point of Trainer display H. Notice that the decimal point is lit for a logic 1 and off for logic 0.

```
00001                              NAM    INPUT-02 REV. 0.2
00002                              OPT    NOP
00003 0000 B6 OF80 REDO            LDA A  $0F80      GET DATA
00004 0003 B7 C167                 STA A  $C167      STORE IT
00005 0006 20 F8                   BRA    REDO       GO BACK AGAIN
00006                              END
```

Figure 132
Program to follow and display input from
data switch 0.

DISCUSSION

Refer again to the circuit in Figure 130. It is quite similar to the one used for outputting data. However, it operates like **read only memory**, with its data being influenced by external sources, (the "outside world").

The circuit is partially decoded as shown in Figure 133. When any of the specified addresses are selected, the buffer drivers of IC1 are enabled through inverter IC2A. This allows the data switch logic to be coupled to the Trainer data bus buffers. As soon as the R/$\overline{\text{W}}$ line goes high (MPU read), gate IC2B enables the input portion of the Trainer data bus buffers through the $\overline{\text{RE}}$ line.

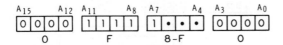

Figure 133

Decoding chart for the first input circuit.

You may have noticed one flaw in the circuit. The buffers in IC1 are always enabled when any of the circuit decoded addresses are selected. Therefore, it is important that you as the programmer do not try to write to these addresses. If you did so, the buffers would try to source or sink the data lines and result in possible circuit damage. One way to avoid this problem is to disconnect pin 4 of IC3 from A_7 and connect it to the R/W line. This will disable IC1 during an MPU write, but the circuit address coding is now changed to $00001111\cdots0000_{16}$.

Both programs in this experiment used address $0F80_{16}$ as an input port. The first retrieves data from $0F80_{16}$ and stores it at 0100_{16}.

The second program also retrieves data from $0F80_{16}$. But this time, it is stored at $C167_{16}$, the address of the decimal point for Trainer display H. Since only the D_0 data bit is connected to the Trainer display, data switch 0 is the only switch to affect the display. The program continuously branches back and retrieves switch data immediately after storing the previous data. Thus, when you changed the position of data switch 0, the decimal point appeared to follow the logic value of the changing switch position.

Next, some additional hardware and software features will be added to the circuit.

PROCEDURE (Continued)

11. Refer to Figure 134 and construct the circuit shown. This circuit interconnects with the first circuit you constructed. Remember, the pushbutton pins are fragile. Press straight down when you install them in the large connector block, mounted on the Trainer cabinet.

12. Position all of the Trainer binary data switches up to logic 1.

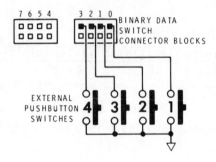

Figure 134
Added circuitry for the data input experiment.

13. Load the program listed in Figure 135, beginning at address 0000_{16} (program step 00007).

14. Execute the program beginning at address 0000_{16}. The decimal point in display C will light to show the program is working.

15. Press one of the four pushbuttons and note the displayed result.

16. Simultaneously press any two pushbuttons and note the result.

17. Simultaneously press any three pushbuttons and note the result.

18. Simultaneously press all four pushbuttons and note the result.

```
00001                           NAM     KEYINDIC REV.0.2
00002                           OPT     NOP
00003 0000                      ORG     0
00004      FE3A    OUTCH   EQU     $FE3A
00005      FE52    OUTSTR  EQU     $FE52
00006      FCBC    REDIS   EQU     $FCBC
00007 0000 BD 0031 ONE     JSR     CLRDIS    CLEAR DISPLAY ROUTINE
00008 0003 BD FCBC         JSR     REDIS     RESET DIGIT POSITION (LEFT)
00009 0006 F6 0F80         LDA B   $0F80     LOOKING FOR KEY CLOSURE
00010 0009 86 30           LDA A   #$30      BIT PATTERN FOR #1
00011 000B 56              ROR B             MOVES "DO" BIT TO C REGISTER
00012 000C 25 02           BCS     TWO       NOT ONE? GO TO TWO
00013 000E 8D 17           BSR     XECUTE    OUTPUT A #1
00014 0010 86 6D   TWO     LDA A   #$6D      BIT PATTERN FOR #2
00015 0012 56              ROR B             MOVES "D1" BIT TO C REGISTER
00016 0013 25 02           BCS     THREE     NOT TWO? GO TO THREE
00017 0015 8D 10           BSR     XECUTE    OUTPUT A #2
00018 0017 86 79   THREE   LDA A   #$79      BIT PATTERN FOR #3
00019 0019 56              ROR B             MOVES "D2" BIT TO C REGISTER
00020 001A 25 02           BCS     FOUR      NOT THREE? GO TO FOUR
00021 001C 8D 09           BSR     XECUTE    OUTPUT A #3
00022 001E 86 33   FOUR    LDA A   #$33      BIT PATTERN FOR #4
00023 0020 56              ROR B             MOVES "D3" BIT TO C REGISTER
00024 0021 25 DD           BCS     ONE       NOT FOUR? GO BACK TO ONE
00025 0023 8D 02           BSR     XECUTE    OUTPUT A #4
00026 0025 20 D9           BRA     ONE       RETURN, RECHECK FOR CLOSURE
00027 0027 BD FE3A XECUTE  JSR     OUTCH     MONITOR ROUTINE OUTPUTS CHAR.
00028 002A CE 0100         LDX     #$0100    ENTER TIMING LOOP
00029 002D 09      HOLD    DEX               TIME RUNNING OUT
00030 002E 26 FD           BNE     HOLD      TIME OUT YET?
00031 0030 39              RTS               RETURN, RECHECK FOR CLOSURE
00032 0031 BD FE52 CLRDIS  JSR     OUTSTR    THE FOLLOWING CLEARS DISPLAY
00033 0034 00              FCB     00,00,00,00,00,$80
      0035 00
      0036 00
      0037 00
      0038 00
      0039 80
00034 003A 39              RTS
00035                      END
```

Figure 135

Program to display the pushbutton numbers in a sequential manner.

DISCUSSION

The four pushbuttons in this experiment simply provide a convenient substitute for the four Trainer data switches. You could obtain the same result by manipulating the data switches. However, the pushbuttons will be needed in the next portion of the experiment.

The program shown in Figure 135 makes extensive use of the Trainer monitor routines located in ROM. These include OUTCH, OUTSTR, and REDIS. An earlier programming experiment showed how to use these routines.

Recall that OUTCH outputs a 7-segment code from accumulator A to the display indicated by a display pointer. OUTSTR outputs a string of characters to the displays. REDIS resets the display pointer so that the first character displayed by OUTCH or OUTSTR is in display H.

In addition, the program has two subroutines of its own. CLRDIS (for clear displays) is in addresses 0031_{16} through $003A_{16}$. It uses OUTSTR to clear the six displays. XECUTE is in addresses 0023_{16} through 0030_{16}. It uses OUTCH to display a character and then goes into a short delay.

The program starts at address 0000_{16}. The first instruction jumps the MPU to the CLRDIS subroutine. After the displays are cleared, the MPU returns to the instruction at address 0003_{16}. This instruction directs the MPU to the REDIS subroutine. This sets the display pointer to display H.

The MPU returns to the instruction in address 0006_{16}. Pushbutton data is now loaded into the B accumulator. Next, the 7-segment pattern for a "1" is loaded in the A accumulator. The D_0 bit in the B accumulator is examined. If it is a one (#1 pushbutton not pressed), the program branches foward to TWO. If the D_0 bit is a zero, the program branches to XECUTE. XECUTE displays the 1 in display H.

After XECUTE, an RTS sends the program back to address 0010_{16}. The A accumulator is loaded with the bit pattern for the digit "2". Then the B accumulator is again rolled right to test for a #2 pushbutton actuation. If #2 was pushed, it will be displayed; otherwise, the program will advance and test the remaining pushbuttons.

The pushbuttons that test true determine the numbers displayed. However, the display pointer determines the display that contains the number.

After all of the pushbuttons have been tested, the display is cleared and the display pointer again points to display H.

In many applications, the MPU constantly scans the input switches looking for input data. However, in some applications this would waste too much of the MPU's time. A better approach is to let the MPU ignore the keyboard until a key is depressed. This is possible through the use of interrupts. In the next part of the experiment you will see how a keyboard can control the MPU through the interrupt line. You will also see how a debounce subroutine works.

PROCEDURE (Continued)

19.   Switch the Trainer power off. Then refer to Figure 136 and add the circuit shown to the circuit already wired to the Trainer. There should be enough room near the left end of the large connector block "on board" the Trainer to hold the additional 74LS30. Notice that the inputs to the 74LS30 are connected in parallel with the data lines leaving the four pushbutton switches. IC2C is one of the unused gates in IC2.

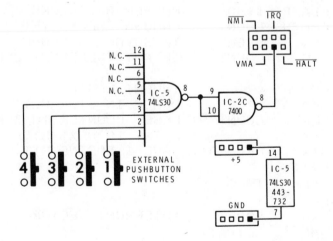

Figure 136
Interrupt circuitry for data input experiment circuit.

20. Switch Trainer power on. Then refer to Figure 137 and enter the program listed beginning at address 0000_{16}. Notice that after you enter the $3B_{16}$ at address $002B_{16}$, you must go to address $00F7_{16}$ to enter the remaining data. 002C and $002D_{16}$ are temporary registers.

21. Now enter 00_{16} into address 0100 thru 0110_{16}. These addresses are used as data storage registers.

22. Execute the program beginning at address 0000_{16}. The display will go blank.

23. Strike each pushbutton sequentially in a 1, 2, 3, 4 order. When you strike each button, use a moderate force, such as you would use when typing with a mechanical typewriter. The data you entered is stored in memory and will not be displayed.

```
00001                        NAM     DBOUNCE1 REV. 0.4
00002                        OPT     NOP
00003          OF80   INPUT  EQU     $0F80
00004   0000  0E           CLI                 READY FOR INTERRUPT
00005   0001  CE 0100 PROGRA LDX     #$0100     POINT TO STORAGE
00006   0004  01           NOP                 *
00007   0005  01           NOP                 * LOCATION FOR PROGRAM
00008   0006  20 F9        BRA     PROGRA      *
00009   0008  B6 OF80 GETDAT LDA A  INPUT      GET DATA
00010   000B  B1 002C      CMP A   TEMP       IS IT LIKE BEFORE?
00011   000E  27 07        BEQ     SAME       IF SO, GO TO SAME
00012   0010  B7 002C      STA A   TEMP       IF NOT, STORE IN TEMP
00013   0013  7F 002D      CLR     COUNT      RESET COUNTER TO ZERO
00014   0016  3B           RTI
00015   0017  C6 40   SAME  LDA B   #$40       NUMBER OF CHECKS
00016   0019  F1 002D      CMP B   COUNT      ENOUGH CHECKS YET?
00017   001C  27 04        BEQ     LEGAL      IF SO,GO TO LEGAL
00018   001E  7C 002D      INC     COUNT      IF NOT,INCREMENT COUNT
00019   0021  3B           RTI
00020   0022  43      LEGAL COM A             INVERT LOGIC
00021   0023  A7 00        STA A   X          PLACE IN STORAGE
00022   0025  7F 002D      CLR     COUNT      RESET COUNTER TO ZERO
00023   0028  08           INX                POINT TO NEXT STORAGE PLACE
00024   0029  DF 02        STX     PROGRA+1 SAVE I DURING RTI
00025   002B  3B           RTI
00026   002C  0001   TEMP   RMB     1
00027   002D  0001   COUNT  RMB     1
00028   00F7                ORG     $00F7      INTERRUPT VECTOR
00029   00F7  7E 0008      JMP     GETDAT
00030                      END
```

Figure 137

Program to software debounce the input
pushbuttons.

24. Examine address 0003_{16}. It should contain 04_{16}, which is the number of pushbutton contact closures made. Change the contents back to 00_{16}.

25. Examine addresses 0100 thru 0103_{16}. They should contain 01, 02, 04, and 08_{16} respectively. Change the data in these four locations back to 00_{16}. Even though the pushbuttons are labeled 1, 2, 3, and 4, they are connected to data lines D_0, D_1, D_2, and D_3. Therefore, the switches will enter the binary values 1, 2, 4, and 8.

26. Execute the program. Then press each pushbutton twice in succession (1, 1, 2, 2, 3, 3, 4, 4). Address 0003_{16} now contains 08_{16}, representing eight pushbutton contact closures. Enter 00_{16} at address 0003_{16}.

27. Examine addresses 0100 thru 0107_{16}. They will show the value of each pushbutton pressed and the sequence it was pressed. Change the data in these address back to 00_{16}.

28. Examine address 0018_{16}. It should contain data 40_{16}. Change the value to 00_{16}.

29. Execute the program. Then press each pushbutton once in sequence.

30. Examine address 0003_{16} and record the contents. $\_\_{}_{16}$. This number should equal 04_{16}. However, it may be higher.

31. Record the data in the following addresses. You need only examine the number of addresses that correspond to the value recorded in step 30.

0100	_ _	0109	_ _
0101	_ _	010A	_ _
0102	_ _	010B	_ _
0103	_ _	010C	_ _
0104	_ _	010D	_ _
0105	_ _	010E	_ _
0106	_ _	010F	_ _
0107	_ _	0110	_ _
0108	_ _		

DISCUSSION

IC5 and gate IC2C provide an interface between the four external pushbuttons and the interrupt request line ($\overline{IRQ}$). The remaining circuitry functions as before. Thus, whenever you attempt to enter data with the pushbutton switches, a request for program interrupt signal is sent to the microprocessor.

The program listed in Figure 137 processes the interrupt and debounces the keys. The program is actually two programs in one. The first part (steps 00005 through 00008) serves as a "simulated" program that runs in an eternal loop until it is interrupted. The remaining program steps actually service the input data pushbuttons during the interrupt. This is the program we will deal with.

Figure 138 is a flow chart for the interrupt program. The numbers at each block represent the assembled program steps.

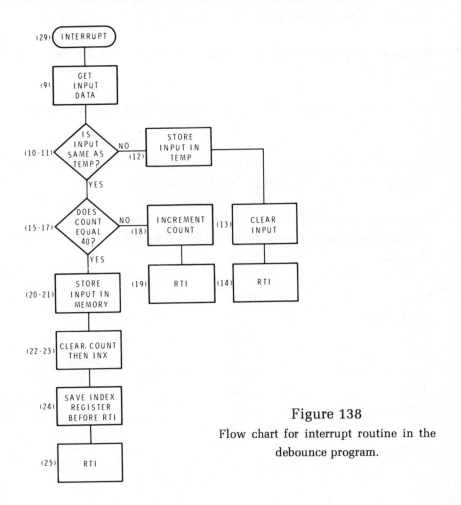

Figure 138
Flow chart for interrupt routine in the debounce program.

When the MPU receives an interrupt request; it completes the instruction it is presently performing, loads the internal registers and accumulators into the stack, sets the interrupt mask in the condition code register, then examines ROM to find out where the program counter is to be vectored. The vector address instruction sends the program counter to the beginning address of the interrupt program.

Pushbutton data is loaded and compared to the data in the temporary register (address $002C_{16}$). Since this is the first time data is examined, there can be no match. Therefore, the pushbutton data is stored in the temporary register, the counter register (address $002D_{16}$) is reset, and the MPU returns to the original program. This is the first time the MPU looks at the pushbuttons during the debounce routine. The data in the temporary register will serve as the reference for all future interrupts. If the input data changes, this new data will be entered, and the counter register will be reset. The counter is used later in the interrupt program to monitor the number of data examinations performed.

Upon return from the interrupt program, the MPU pulls the accumulator and register data from the stack. This clears the interrupt mask, and since you still have the pushbutton pressed, the MPU immediately acknowledges the interrupt request. Whereupon, it stores into the stack, sets the mask, and looks up the interrupt vector.

Pushbutton data is again compared with the temporary register. This time, it matches. Thus, allowing a branch to address 0017_{16}. Data 40_{16} is loaded into the B accumulator and then compared with the count register. Since the count is zero, there is no match. Therefore, the count is incremented and the MPU returns to the main program.

Assuming you are still holding the pushbutton down, the MPU goes through the interrupt routine 38 more times (39 total). During the 40th cycle, if the data is still good, the MPU will be satisfied that the data supplied by the pushbutton is true, and the program is allowed to branch to address 0022_{16}.

The contents of accumulator A (pushbutton data) is complemented and stored at the address pointed to by the index register. This address was loaded into the index register in the main program. It is the first of 17_{10} addresses you reserved for data when you performed the experiment.

The counter register is cleared (in case the same pushbutton is again pressed). The index register is incremented and stored at address 0002_{16}. This points to the next data address, in preparation for the next pushbutton closure. Finally, the MPU returns to the main program.

You may have wondered why the pushbutton data was complemented before storage (address 0022_{16}). This was necessary since the pushbuttons were wired using inverse logic. That is, when the #1 pushbutton was pressed, data $1111\ 1110_2$ was transferred on the data bus, rather than $0000\ 0001_2$. Thus, it was necessary to invert the data for "logical" interpretation.

In the second part of this portion of the experiment, you changed the number of data examinations from 40_{16} to 00_{16} (address 0018_{16}). Then when you entered four pushbutton closures, you probably found more than four entries stored at address 0003_{16}. This occurred because the contacts of a switch tend to bounce open and closed a number of times before they stay closed. Since the bounce period can last many milliseconds, the MPU could treat each bounce as a separate entry, as you probably experienced.

Again look at the data you recorded in step 31. As you know, the program is designed to store one pushbutton closure in each address. A series of two or more identical entries indicates bounce. You may even have one or two zeroes recorded. This occurred because the contacts opened after an interrupt request, but before the data could be tested. Thus, a zero is stored.

Contact bounce can not be tolerated. But, what is a desirable number of switch samples? This will depend on the type of switch. If the sample is too low, bounce can occasionally get through. Large samples waste time and may require long switch hold-down periods. Normally five to eight samples are sufficient for a program of the type you used in this experiment. However, some switches will produce excessive bounce. As a precaution, 40 samples are used in the program.

Your Microprocessor Trainer uses a similar software routine for key debounce. This is stored in its ROM. Another method for debouncing a switch is to use cross-coupled NAND gates. They latch on the first closure and any additional bouncing is ignored. Regardless of the method used, you must debounce any mechanical switch used for data entry.

If you experiment with the sample rates in the program you entered, always be sure to change the data at addresses 0003_{16} and 0100 through 0110_{16} to 00_{16} before you execute the program.

PROCEDURE (Continued)

32. This completes this experiment. Switch the Trainer power off. Then remove all of the hookup wire and components from the two large connector blocks.

Experiment 16

Introduction to the Peripheral Interface Adapter (PIA)

OBJECTIVES:

> *Show how to interface the MPU with the outside world using a PIA (6820).*

> *Demonstrate various ways the PIA can be initialized as an input, output, or input/output (I/O) device.*

INTRODUCTION

As you have seen in the previous experiments, the need for latches and drivers to communicate with the MPU from the outside world can become quite burdensome. Then, once you have established a hardware interface circuit, you can not easily modify its function. However, the PIA can simplify your interface requirements in such a way that standardization is possible regardless of application. Therefore, you can easily develop interface systems compatible with your hardware and software needs. This is possible because most of the PIA performance characteristics are software controlled. Thus, performance and design features can be modified with little difficulty. In this experiment, some of the PIA's characteristics will be examinded.

MATERIAL REQUIRED

1   ET-3400 Microprocessor Trainer

2   1000 ohm, 1/4-watt, 10% resistors

1   7400 integrated circuit (443-1)

1   74LS30 integrated circuit (443-732)

1   74LS27 integrated circuit (443-800)

1   6820 PIA integrated circuit (443-843)

Hookup wire

PROCEDURE

1. Make sure the Trainer power is off. Then construct the circuit shown in Figure 139. Caution: The PIA is a MOS device and should be handled properly.

2. Carefully reexamine the circuit you constructed. There should be a wire connected to each lead of the PIA.

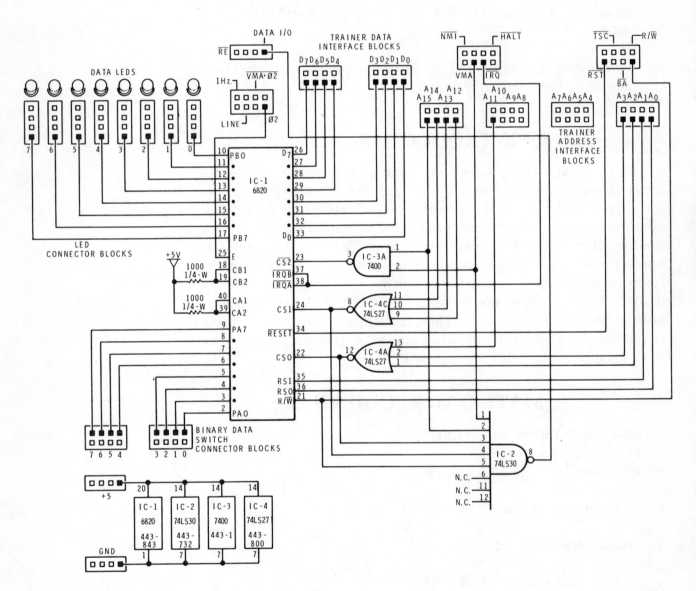

Figure 139
Circuit diagram for the first PIA experiment.

3. Switch the Trainer power on. Then enter the program listed in Figure 140.

4. Set all of the binary data switches to their down (logic 0) position. Then execute the program. The display will go blank.

5. Randomly set the data switches and observe the data LED's. Notice that the LED corresponding to each switch follows the logic level of the switch.

6. Change the instruction at address 0017_{16} to 43_{16}.

7. Execute the program and again randomly set the data switches. Notice that the data LED's now show the complement logic level of the switches.

8. Refer to Figure 140 and briefly describe the "service routine" section of the program. _____

_____

_____

_____

_____

_____

_____

```
00001                           NAM     PIA-EXP1 REV. 0.2
00002                           OPT     NOP
00003                      *INITIALIZE PIA
00004  0000  86 00             LDA A   #00          0=INPUT
00005  0002  B7 8000           STA A   $8000        A SIDE NOW INPUT
00006  0005  86 04             LDA A   #04          SET TO COMMUN.
00007  0007  B7 8001           STA A   $8001
00008  000A  86 FF             LDA A   #$FF         1=OUTPUT
00009  000C  B7 8002           STA A   $8002        B SIDE NOW OUTPUT
00010  000F  86 04             LDA A   #04          SET TO COMMUN.
00011  0011  B7 8003           STA A   $8003
00012                      *SERVICE ROUTINE
00013  0014  B6 8000    RESERV LDA A   $8000        GET DATA
00014  0017  01                NOP
00015  0018  B7 8002           STA A   $8002        STORE TO OUTPUT
00016  001B  20 F7             BRA     RESERV       DO IT AGAIN
00017                          END
```

Figure 140

Program to initialize and use the PIA for

data input and output.

DISCUSSION

By now you are quite familiar with address decoding. Therefore, the discussion will deal with the PIA. Figure 141 is a decoding chart for the circuit you wired to the Trainer. If during this discussion you don't fully understand a specific function of the PIA, refer to the PIA section in Unit 8 and the PIA data sheet in Appendix B.

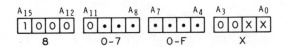

Figure 141
Decoding chart for the circuit in Figure 140.

Three chip-select pins on the PIA provide for easy decoding. They help eliminate address decoding gates. In small systems where partial address decoding can be tolerated, these three pins may be all that is needed to access the device. Notice that the PIA responds to addresses 8000_{16} through 8003_{16}.

The reset pin clears the PIA registers and is normally used at system turn-on. Therefore, it is connected to the system reset line.

The read/write pin controls data flow direction in the PIA in a manner similar to the RAM. Thus, it is connected to the R/W line from the MPU.

Interrupt request lines A and B can be wire OR'ed as in this experiment. Thus, each can transmit an MPU interrupt on the $\overline{NMI}$ or $\overline{IRQ}$ lines (in this experiment, the feature is not used).

Control pins A1 and B1 are inputs that are used to control the internal PIA interrupt flags. Control pins A2 and B2 can also serve as interrupt inputs or as peripheral control outputs. Since these features are not required for this experiment, each pin is pulled to a logic 1 to provide a termination and prevent undesired PIA interrupts.

The enable pin controls data transfer between the PIA and MPU. Since MPU data transfer occurs during time $\phi 2$, this pin is connected to Trainer $\phi 2$.

Data pins 0 through 7 are connected to the MPU data bus for device communication.

Peripheral pins A0 through A7 can be programmed as inputs or outputs. In this experiment, they are programmed as inputs and are connected to the binary data switches.

Peripheral pins B0 through B7 can also be programmed as inputs or outputs. In this experiment, they are programmed as outputs and are connected to the data LED's. Normally, the B side is used as an output because of its extra drive capabilities.

As you learned in Unit 8, the PIA must be initialized before it can function properly. This is accomplished through a software routine. Because initialization is accomplished by software, the PIA's operation can be modified at any time during the program.

When the PIA receives a reset pulse, its six memory accessible registers are cleared. Thus, whenever the Trainer RESET key is pressed, the PIA is reset. Because of this, the PIA must be initialized after each reset.

The program you entered (Figure 140) used the instructions in addresses 0000 through 0013_{16} to initialize the PIA. This programs the A side of the PIA as an input. Then, 04_{16} was loaded into control register A. This sets bit 2 of the control register high, which isolates the data direction register and accesses the output register.

In a like manner, the B side of the PIA is set up as an output by loading FF_{16} into the data direction register. Then the data direction register is isolated and the output register accessed by loading 04_{16} into the control register.

The remaining steps in the program comprise the service routine. The MPU reads data from the A side of the PIA and stores it to the B side. The "branch always" instruction holds the program in the service routine. Once the PIA is initialized, it will function as programmed until it is reset.

When you changed the instruction at address 0017_{16} to 43_{16}, you instructed the MPU to complement the data in the A accumulator before storing the data.

The program listed in Figure 142 is the same as the program you used, with one exception; the index register is used in place of the A accumulator for initializing the PIA. This reduced the number of program steps required.

```
00001                              NAM     PIA-EXP2 REV. 0.2
00002                              OPT     NOP
00003                      *INITIALIZE PIA
00004  0000 CE 0004               LDX     #$0004
00005  0003 FF 8000               STX     $8000
00006  0006 CE FF04               LDX     #$FF04
00007  0009 FF 8002               STX     $8002
00008                      *SERVICE ROUTINE
00009  000C B6 8000  RESERV LDA A   $8000     GET DATA
00010  000F 01                     NOP
00011  0010 B7 8002         STA A   $8002     STORE TO OUTPUT
00012  0013 20 F7           BRA     RESERV    DO IT AGAIN
00013                              END
```

Figure 142

Alternate program to initialize the PIA for

data input/output.

PROCEDURE (Continued)

9.   Do not disassemble the circuit you have wired to the Trainer. It will be used in the next experiment. Proceed to Experiment 17.

Experiment 17

Audio Output

OBJECTIVES:

Show how a transducer can be interfaced with an MPU.

Provide an opportunity to write an output program that will supply the data to drive a speaker.

Demonstrate how different audible tones can be generated.

INTRODUCTION

With the proper interface, microprocessors are capable of producing meaningful audio sounds. These signals are often useful as indicators when the operator cannot monitor the display and would like to know when an event has occured.

Audible sounds can be produced in two ways. The first simply uses a buzzer that is activated by a change in output logic level, in the same manner as an LED. The second method actually drives an audio speaker. This experiment will use the second method to produce a variety of meaningful tones.

MATERIALS REQUIRED

1   ET-3400 Microprocessor Trainer with PIA circuit wired to the large connector block

2   100 ohm, 1/2-watt, 10% resistors

1   100 μF electrolytic capacitor

1   Speaker

Foam tape (from previous experiment)

Solder (from Trainer kit)

Hookup wire

PROCEDURE

1. Cut two 14″ hookup wires and remove 1/4″ of insulation from the ends of each wire. Then twist the wires together, leaving about 2″ untwisted at each end.

2. Remove the speaker from its packing container. Then refer to Figure 143 and solder the two wires at one end of the 14″ twisted wire pair to the two speaker terminals. Disregard any polarity marks on the speaker.

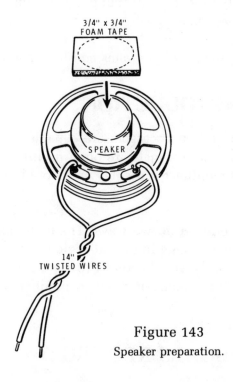

Figure 143
Speaker preparation.

3. Cut a 3/4″ × 3/4″ piece of foam tape. Remove the paper backing from one side and press the tape onto the end of the magnet on the speaker. Then remove the paper backing from the other side of the tape and affix the speaker to the sloping back of the Trainer cabinet near the Power switch. Position the speaker lugs up away from the Trainer.

4. Switch the Trainer power off. Remove the eight wires interconnecting the data LED's and PIA. Then remove the eight wires interconnecting the binary data switches and PIA.

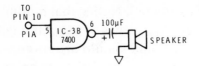

Figure 144

Speaker/PIA interface circuit.

5. Refer to Figure 144 and construct the circuit shown. Connect the speaker wires and the capacitor to the unused large connector block. (Additional components will be added later in the experiment.) The gate is part of IC3 in the original circuit. You can use pin 7 of IC3 for speaker ground. Figure 145 shows the complete circuit wired to your Trainer.

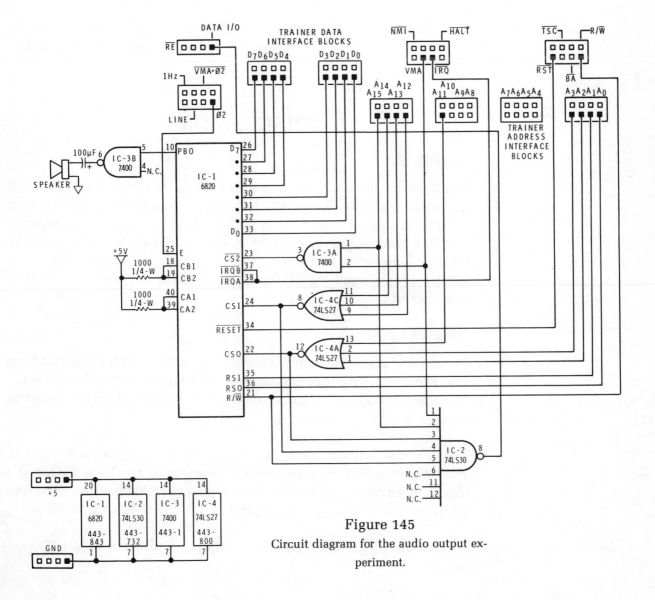

Figure 145

Circuit diagram for the audio output experiment.

6. Switch the Trainer power on. Load the program listed in Figure 146. Begin at address 0003_{16} (line 00008). Notice that a number of program steps have no data entry. Also, lines 00027_{16} and 00052_{16} contain assembler equate statements and should be ignored. After you enter 20_{16} at address $004B_{16}$, go to address $00F7_{16}$ to enter $3B_{16}$.

7. Press RESET, then install a hookup wire between LINE and $\overline{IRQ}$. This wire is not shown in the circuit diagram.

8. The program you entered is for a clock function. Addresses 0000, 0001, and 0002_{16} are reserved for the seconds, minutes, and hours of the clock respectively. Enter the desired time into these three addresses.

9. Execute the program beginning at address 0003_{16}. Each time the seconds count updates, you should hear a "tick" from the speaker.

DISCUSSION

HARDWARE

Gate IC3B supplies the current needed to drive the speaker, while the 100 μF capacitor protects the gate. If the program stopped during a logic high output, the speaker would act as a direct short to ground. The capacitor coupling prevents this possibility. A side benefit of the capacitor is the RC time constant it forms with the internal gate circuitry. The pulse width for logic 1 and logic 0 transitions is different, producing a "tick-tock" sound.

SOFTWARE

The clock program you entered is very similar to the clock program from Experiment 12. Two instructions were added to initialize the PIA (lines 00008 and 00009). Also, a store instruction was added to the 60-second timer subroutine (line 00022).

The store instruction outputs the seconds digit information to the PIA (B side) every time the digit increments. Since the D_0 data bit is the only bit that changes during each time update, only peripheral output PB0 (pin 10) is needed to supply speaker data.

If you have any questions concerning the clock program, refer to Experiment 12.

```
00001                           NAM     CLOCK-3  * REV  0.2
00002            **LINE ACCURACY CLOCK PROGRAM
00003                           OPT     NOP
00004 0000 0001  SECOND RMB     1
00005 0001 0001  MINUTE RMB     1
00006 0002 0001  HOURS  RMB     1
00007            ** PIA INITIALIZATION
00008 0003 CE FF04              LDX     #$FF04
00009 0006 FF 8002              STX     $8002
00010            ** INTERRUPT HANDLING
00011 0009 CE 003D TIMPAS LDX   #$003D  61
00012 000C 09     ONE60T DEX            TIME TICKING OFF
00013 000D 27 04         BEQ    TIMEUP  60 PULSES YET?
00014 000F 0E            CLI
00015 0010 3E            WAI            WAITING
00016 0011 20 F9         BRA    ONE60T  GO BACK & WAIT AGAIN!
00017            ** INCR ONE SECOND AND UPDATE
00018 0013 C6 60  TIMEUP LDA B  #$60    SIXTY SECONDS,SIXTY MINUTES
00019 0015 0D            SEC            ALWAYS INCREMENT SECONDS
00020 0016 8D 16         BSR    INCR    INCREMENT SECONDS
00021 0018 96 00         LDA A  SECOND
00022 001A B7 8002       STA A  $8002
00023 001D 8D 0F         BSR    INCR    INCREMENT MINUTES IF NEEDED
00024 001F C6 13         LDA B  #$13    TWELVE HOUR CLOCK
00025 0021 8D 0B         BSR    INCR    INCREMENT HOURS
00026 0023 BD FCBC       JSR    REDIS   RESET DISPLAYS
00027      FCBC   REDIS  EQU    $FCBC
00028 0026 8D 17         BSR    PRINT
00029 0028 8D 15         BSR    PRINT
00030 002A 8D 13         BSR    PRINT   PRINT HOURS,MINUTES,SECONDS
00031 002C 20 DB         BRA    TIMPAS  DO IT ALL AGAIN
00032            ** INCR - INCREMENT SUBROUTINE
00033 002E A6 00  INCR   LDA A  0,X     DATA WORD INTO A
00034 0030 89 00         ADC A  #0      INCREMENT IF NECESSARY
00035 0032 19            DAA            FIX TO DECIMAL
00036 0033 11            CBA            TIME TO CLEAR?
00037 0034 25 01         BCS    INC1    NO
00038 0036 4F            CLR A
00039 0037 A7 00  INC1   STA A  0,X
00040 0039 08            INX
00041 003A 07            TFA
00042 003B 88 01         EOR A  #1      COMPLEMENT CARRY BIT
00043 003D 06            TAP
00044 003E 39            RTS
00045            ** PRINT - PRINT HEX BYTES
00046 003F 09     PRINT  DEX            POINT X AT BYTE
00047 0040 96 02         LDA A  $02     WHAT'S IN HOURS?
00048 0042 26 03         BNE    CONTIN  IF NOT ZERO
00049 0044 7C 0002       INC    HOURS   MAKE IT ONE
00050 0047 A6 00  CONTIN LDA A  0,X
00051 0049 7E FE20       JMP    OUTBYT
00052      FE20   OUTBYT EQU    $FE20   MONITOR ROUTINE
00053 00F7          ORG    $00F7
00054 00F7 3B         RTI
00055               END
```

Figure 146

Clock program with audible tick-tock.

PROCEDURE (Continued)

10. Switch the Trainer power off. Then remove the wire interconnecting LINE and IRQ. Switch the Trainer power on.

11. Write a program that will output the proper data to produce an audio tone from the speaker circuit. This program must: Initialize the PIA, alternately store 1's and 0's to the speaker in order to produce a tone, and provide a delay loop between each storage, to determine the frequency of the tone.

12. Execute the program.

DISCUSSION

Figure 147 shows a program similar to the one you wrote. Notice that only two instructions were required to initialize the PIA. This is possible since only the B side will be used to output data.

Remember from the previous program, it is only necessary to change the D_0 bit of the output data, since that is the only bit connected to the speaker circuit. Therefore, you can start with a random number in the A accumulator (line 00007) and store the number to the PIA. After a short delay (lines 00008 thru 00010) the A accumulator is incremented (changing the D_0 bit logic level) and again stored to the PIA. This incrementing and storing of accumulator A can continue indefinitely since the only data of interest is the D_0 bit.

```
00001                              NAM      TONETEST REV. 0.2
00002                              OPT      NOP
00003                        *INITIALIZE PIA
00004   0000 CE FF04              LDX      #$FF04
00005   0003 FF 8002              STX      $8002
00006                        *PRODUCE TONE
00007   0006 B7 8002  ALTERN STA A  $8002       OUTPUT BIT
00008   0009 C6 55              LDA B    #$55        DETERMINES FREQUENCY
00009   000B 5A        TONE    DEC B
00010   000C 26 FD              BNE      TONE
00011   000E 4C               INC A                  COMP. BIT
00012   000F 20 F5              BRA      ALTERN
00013                              END
```

Figure 147

Program to output a tone through the
speaker.

PROCEDURE (Continued)

13. Enter the program listed in Figure 148. After you enter $F1_{16}$ at address 0024_{16}, go to address 0101_{16} and enter the remaining data bits. Notice that the program covers two pages. The listing on the second page has been condensed to show only the assembled program line numbers, addresses, and data.

14. Execute the program beginning at address 0000_{16}. Notice that after the program completes the song, there is a pause (of equal duration to the song) before the song repeats.

```
00001                         NAM    MUSIC     REV. 0.3
00002 0000                    ORG    0
00003 0000 7F 8003  REPLAY    CLR    $8003     CLEAR CRB-2 BIT
00004 0003 7C 8002            INC    $8002     INCR DATA DIRECTION REG
00005 0006 73 8003            COM    $8003     SET CRB-2 BIT
00006 0009 8E 0100            LDS    #TEMP     POINT TO FIRST NOTE -1
00007 000C CE 05FF  NUNOTE    LDX    #$05FF    TIME PER NOTE
00008 000F 33                 PUL B            PULL NEXT NOTE FROM STACK
00009 0010 5D                 TST B            HAS LAST NOTE BEEN PLAYED?
00010 0011 27 ED              BEQ    REPLAY    IF NOT, CONTINUE
00011 0013 F7 0100            STA B  TEMP      STORE NOTE-CODE
00012 0016 4C       TONLUP    INC A            TOGGLES OUTPUT WHEN STORED
00013 0017 F6 0100            LDA B  TEMP      GET NOTE-CODE
00014 001A 09       COUNT     DEX              HOLD TONE FOR AWHILE
00015 001B 27 EF              BEQ    NUNOTE    LONG ENOUGH YET?
00016 001D 5A                 DEC B
00017 001E 26 FA              BNE    COUNT
00018 0020 B7 8002            STA A  $8002     TOGGLES OUTPUT
00019 0023 20 F1              BRA    TONLUP
00020 0100                    ORG    $0100
00021 0100 0001   TEMP        RMB    1
00022 0101 53                 FCB    $53,$42,$53,$42,$53,$42,$53,$42,$53
      0102 42
      0103 53
      0104 42
      0105 53
      0106 42
      0107 53
      0108 42
      0109 53
00023 010A 42                 FCB    $42,$53,$42,$37,$42,$37,$42,$37,$42
      010B 53
      010C 42
      010D 37
      010E 42
      010F 37
      0110 42
      0111 37
      0112 42
00024 0113 37                 FCB    $37,$42
      0114 42
00025 0115 22                 FCB    $22,$2B,$22,$2B,$20,$29,$20,$29
      0116 2B
      0117 22
      0118 2B
      0119 20
      011A 29
      011B 20
      011C 29
00026 011D 20                 FCB    $20,$29,$20,$29,$20,$29,$20,$29,$20
      011E 29
      011F 20
      0120 29
      0121 20
```

Figure 148

Music program (Part 1 of 2).

	0122	29	00031	014A	4A		0172	4A		019A	46
	0123	20		014B	3E		0173	37		019B	3A
	0124	29		014C	4A		0174	4A		019C	46
	0125	20		014D	3E	00036	0175	31		019D	3E
00027	0126	29		014E	4A		0176	3E		019E	4A
	0127	20		014F	3E		0177	31		019F	3E
	0128	29		0150	4A		0178	3E		01A0	4A
	0129	20		0151	3E		0179	2B		01A1	3E
	012A	29		0152	4A		017A	37	00041	01A2	4A
	012B	20	00032	0153	3E		017B	2B		01A3	3E
	012C	29		0154	4A		017C	37		01A4	4A
	012D	20		0155	3E		017D	2B		01A5	24
	012E	29		0156	4A	00037	017E	37		01A6	3E
00028	012F	20		0157	3E		017F	2B		01A7	24
	0130	29		0158	4A		0180	37		01A8	3E
	0131	2B		0159	3E		0181	2B		01A9	29
	0132	37		015A	4A		0182	37		01AA	42
	0133	2B		015B	3E		0183	2B	00042	01AB	29
	0134	37	00033	015C	4A		0184	37		01AC	42
	0135	24		015D	3E		0185	2B		01AD	29
	0136	2B		015E	4A		0186	37		01AE	42
	0137	24		015F	3E	00038	0187	2B		01AF	29
00029	0138	2B		0160	4A		0188	37		01B0	42
	0139	29		0161	3E		0189	2B		01B1	29
	013A	37		0162	58		018A	37		01B2	42
	013B	29		0163	3E		018B	2B		01B3	29
	013C	37		0164	58		018C	37	00043	01B4	42
	013D	42	00034	0165	3E		018D	2B		01B5	29
	013E	37		0166	58		018E	37		01B6	42
	013F	42		0167	3E		018F	2B		01B7	29
	0140	37		0168	58	00039	0190	37		01B8	42
00030	0141	42		0169	3E		0191	31		01B9	2B
	0142	37		016A	58		0192	3E		01BA	31
	0143	42		016B	3E		0193	31		01BB	37
	0144	37	00035	016C	58		0194	3E		01BC	3E
	0145	3A		016D	37		0195	37	00044	01BD	42
	0146	46		016E	4A		0196	42		01BE	4A
	0147	3A		016F	37		0197	37		01BF	00
	0148	46		0170	4A		0198	42	00045	END	
	0149	3E		0171	37	00040	0199	3A			

Figure 148
Music program (Part 2 of 2).

DISCUSSION

The program you entered occupies memory locations 0000 through 0024_{16}. The remaining data represents the notes in the music. It was structured in this manner so that you could experiment with different songs. Figure 149 illustrates the various notes the program can produce, on the outline of an organ keyboard. Each note is listed with its actual fundamental frequency below the note letter. The number below the frequency is the hex number that will produce that approximate frequency. The notes your Trainer will produce depends on the MPU clock frequency.

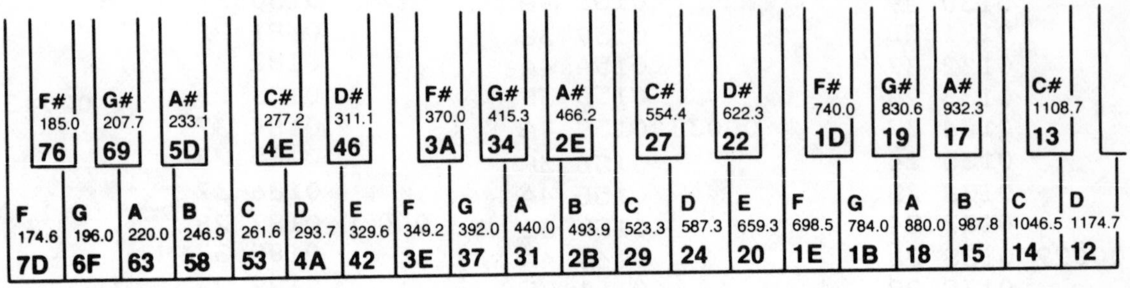

Figure 149

Music notes produced by the program in

Figure 148.

Although the music program is basically simple, there are a few unique features that should be examined. The first instruction clears control register B of the PIA. Naturally, this occurs prior to program execution. However, it will be necessary to modify the contents of data direction register B prior to each program cycle. Thus, bit two in the control register is cleared.

The second instruction turns bit PB0 on or off for each program cycle. Incrementing the data direction register will be of more value in the next section of this experiment.

Instruction four (LDS) tells the MPU that the data stored at 0101 thru $01BF_{16}$ now resides in the stack. However, the pointer contains address 0100_{16}. This is necessary, since each "pull" instruction adds "1" to the pointer prior to execution.

The last note in the stack is 00_{16}. This is used to indicate "end of music." Since a pull instruction does not affect any of the MPU condition codes, it is necessary to test for zero with instruction seven (TST B).

The remaining program steps contain two timing loops. The first, starting at line 00007 sets the music tempo. The second, starting at line 00008 produces the notes.

NOTE: If you wish to listen to your ROM, enter FC_{16} at $000A_{16}$, and 01_{16} at 0010_{16}. It is necessary to remove the TST B instruction, since ROM contains a number of 00_{16} data bytes. Now, the program will continue until you press RESET.

PROCEDURE (Continued)

15.   If you modified the music program (addresses 0000 through 0024_{16}), refer to Figure 148 and reenter the program. It's not necessary to reenter the same music notes if you have not modified them.

16.   Refer to Figure 150 and modify your speaker circuit. Notice that a resistor is placed between gate IC3B and the speaker. Also, an additional gate (from IC3) and resistor interface pin 11 of the PIA with the speaker.

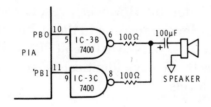

Figure 150
Modification to the speaker circuit.

17.   Execute the music program. This time, the music plays three times before there is a pause. The first repeat is an octave lower, and the second repeat simultaneously plays the original and octave lower music.

DISCUSSION

The gate connected to pin 11 of the PIA (data bit PB1) allows an additional output interface to the speaker. The two resistors reduce circuit loading so the outputs of the two gates can be combined at the coupling capacitor. However, the resistors also reduce the signal level and as a result, speaker volume.

The music program is unchanged from the previous section. However, you are now using two additional features in the program that previously were not required or apparent. The first concerns the PIA. Each time the program repeats, the data direction register bits are incremented. This meant the PB0 bit cycled the music on and off. Now that two output pins are wired to the circuit, a new pattern develops. First, pin PB0 is active. Then pin PB1 is active. Next, both pins are active. Finally both pins are inactive. Thereafter, the cycle repeats.

That cyclic pattern accounts for two (apparent) channels of music. But, why does one channel sound like it is one octave lower in frequency?

At the end of each "note" timing loop, the A accumulator is stored, and then incremented. Thus, the speaker is driven by a cyclic logic level transition of the D_0 data bit. However, every two level transitions in the D_0 bit causes a single level transition in the D_1 bit. Figure 151 illustrates the process. Since bit D_0 is coupled to PIA bit PB0, and bit D_1 is coupled to PIA bit PA1, you effectively have identical music material generated at two different octave levels.

If you have a stereo sound system, you can connect the music output of each gate (through a 100 ohm resistor) to the AUX input of your amplifier. The sound reproduction will be better than that produced by your Trainer.

This completes this experiment. Leave the circuit intact for the next experiment.

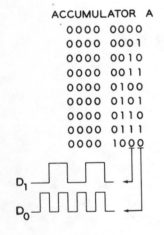

ACCUMULATOR A
```
0000 0000
0000 0001
0000 0010
0000 0011
0000 0100
0000 0101
0000 0110
0000 0111
0000 1000
```

Figure 151
Music material coupled to the PIA.

Experiment 18

Key Matrix and Parallel-to-Serial Conversion

OBJECTIVES:

Demonstrate a method for using any combination of PIA I/O ports as inputs or outputs.

Show how a matrix-type keyboard decoder system works, and how it can be constructed.

Demonstrate parallel-to-serial conversion using the PIA.

Demonstrate a method for converting a hex digit to ASCII.

Show how a "one-shot" monostable works, using software.

Show how to add the parity bit to a serial word, using software.

INTRODUCTION

You are quite familiar with the PIA by now. In this experiment, you will demonstrate its versatility as an I/O device. In addition to using one peripheral port as both an input and output bus, you will see how a parallel data transfer device can be used to communicate in "serial." Since a great amount of serial data uses ASCII, this experiment will use the ASCII format.

MATERIAL REQUIRED

1   ET-3400 Microprocessor Trainer with PIA circuit wired to the large connector block

2   1000 ohm, 1/4-watt, 10% resistors

1   Pushbutton switch #1

1   Pushbutton switch #2

1   Pushbutton switch #3

1   Pushbutton switch #4

PROCEDURE

1.   In this part of the experiment, you will see how the PIA interfaces with a switch matrix. Switch the Trainer power off. Then remove the 100 μF capacitor, two 100 ohm resistors, speaker and the wires associated with those parts.

2.   Refer to Figure 152 and add the circuit shown to the PIA circuit. Figure 153 shows the complete circuit wired to your Trainer.

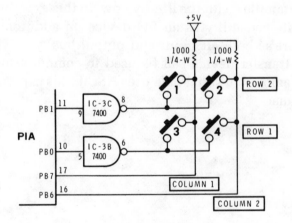

Figure 152
Matrix switch circuit.

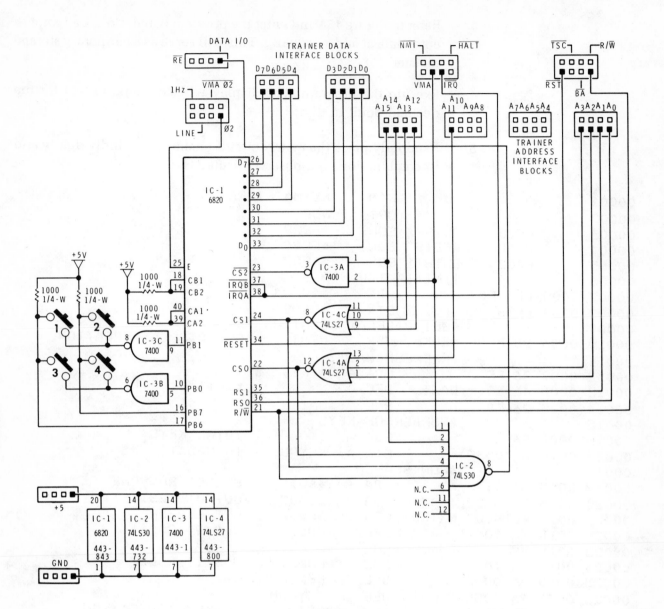

Figure 153
Circuit diagram for the switch matrix decoding circuit.

3. Refer to Figure 154 and enter the program listed. Do not attempt to enter data at address $003E_{16}$. This will serve as a temporary storage register.

4. Execute the program. The display will go blank, except for the decimal point in digit H.

5. Randomly press the matrix circuit pushbuttons, individually and in combination, and observe display H.

```
00001                    NAM      KEYMATRI REV 0.4
00002                    OPT      NOF
00003      FE28   OUTHEX EQU      $FE28
00004      FCBC   REDIS  EQU      $FCBC
00005      FE52   OUTST1 EQU      $FE52
00006             *INITIALIZE PIA
00007 0000 CE 0F04        LDX     #$0F04
00008 0003 FF 8002        STX     $8002
00009             *SET DISPLAY LOCATION
00010 0006 BD FCBC NEWKEY JSR     REDIS        SET DISPLAY LOCATION
00011             *REFRESH WAIT
00012 0009 86 FF          LDA A   #$FF         *
00013 000B 4A      WAIT   DEC A                *WAIT
00014 000C 26 FD          BNE     WAIT         *
00015             *NUMBER OF KEYS
00016 000E 86 04          LDA A   #$04         TOTAL KEYS
00017 0010 B7 003E        STA A   KEYNUM       TO UPDATE
00018             *ROW SEARCH
00019 0013 86 01          LDA A   #$01         SELECT ROW,ONE
00020 0015 B7 8002        STA A   $8002        OUTPUT TEST BIT
00021 0018 F6 8002 NXTROW LDA B   $8002        GET CLOSURE
00022 001B 2A 10          BPL     COL1         WAS IT COL1?
00023 001D 59             ROL B
00024 001E 2A 10          BPL     COL2         WAS IT COL2?
00025 0020 7A 003E        DEC     KEYNUM
00026 0023 7A 003E        DEC     KEYNUM
00027 0026 27 10          BEQ     OUT          NO KEY INDICATION
00028 0028 78 8002        ASL     $8002        SHFT ROW BIT
00029 002B 20 EB          BRA     NXTROW       TEST NEXT ROW
00030             *COLUMN IDENTIFICATION
00031 002D 7A 003E COL1   DEC     KEYNUM
00032 0030 B6 003E COL2   LDA A   KEYNUM       GET KEY NUMBER
00033 0033 BD FE28        JSR     OUTHEX       MONITOR ROUTINE
00034 0036 20 CE          BRA     NEWKEY
00035             *BLANK DISPLAY
00036 0038 BD FE52 OUT    JSR     OUTST1       MONITOR ROUTINE
00037 003B 80             FCB     $80          OUTPUT D.P. ONLY
00038 003C 20 C8          BRA     NEWKEY
00039 003E 0001   KEYNUM  RMB     1            NUMBER TO BE DISPLAYED
00040                     END
```

Figure 154
Program for decoding key matrix.

DISCUSSION

Refer to Figure 152. Notice that each pushbutton switch occupies a unique row and column electrically. Referring to the switch contacts, each "column" line is held at a logic 1 through a 1000 ohm resistor. Each "row" line is held at a logic 1 by the output of a NAND gate. In this circuit, the gates serve as inverter/drivers.

Assume that you close switch 2. In searching for the closed switch, the program first places a logic 0 on row 1 and then examines column 1 and column 2. Since both columns are still at a logic 1, row 1 is returned to logic 1, and row 2 is pulled to a logic 0. Again columns 1 and 2 are examined. This time, column 2 is found to be low, indicating that switch 2 is closed.

Refer to the program in Figure 154. Data direction register B is loaded with a bit pattern ($0F_{16}$) that sets pins PB0 and PB1 as outputs, and pins PB6 and PB7 as inputs. Although the other pins are set, they are not used in this experiment. Bit pattern 04_{16} then sets bit 2 of the control register high for access to the peripheral B interface.

A jump to monitor routine REDIS stores the address of display H in a temporary location in memory. This address will be used by other monitor routines to output data to display H.

The next three instructions provide a short time delay to help prevent character "ghosting." Some ghosting may be noticed in subdued light, due to the "rewriting" techniques used in this program.

Since four pushbutton switches (keys) are used in this experiment, decimal 4 is stored at temporary register 0041_{16}. This number or a decremented value of this number will be displayed when a switch closure is recognized.

The row search begins by storing 01_{16} to the PIA. This pulls the output of IC3B low (row 1). Then the PIA B side bus data is loaded into the B accumulator, and bit D_7 is tested for a 0. Assuming switch 2 was pressed, bit D_7 will test as a 1. The B accumulator is rotated left so that bit D_6 can be tested at the D_7 position. Since it also indicates 1, switches 3 and 4 have tested open.

Key number 4 in the temporary register (0041_{16}) is decremented twice prior to testing switches 1 and 2. Data stored at the PIA is shifted left. This pulls row 2 low.

The row search begins again at line 00021. When column 2 is tested, it is discovered that switch 2 is closed. The program branches to address 0033_{16}, and the A accumulator is loaded with the key number (2) from the temporary register. The monitor routine, OUTHEX, writes the number 2 into display H, and branches back to address 0006_{16} where the program begins again.

If all of the keys test open during row search, the program will branch to OUT, where a monitor routine lights the decimal point in display H and blanks all of the other displays. Then, the program branches back to address 0006_{16} and begins again.

You may have noticed that as you press more than one switch, the first switch tested will have priority. This occurs in a 3, 4, 1, 2 sequence.

Up to 16 switches can be tested with this program. By using both the A and B sides of the PIA, up to 64 switches can be tested. This can represent a big savings in peripheral interface logic.

PROCEDURE (Continued)

6.   Switch the Trainer power off. Then remove the four switches, their two 1000 ohm resistors, and their associated wires. This includes the wires at pins 10 and 11 of the PIA.

7.   Add the circuit shown in Figure 155 to the PIA circuit wired to your Trainer.

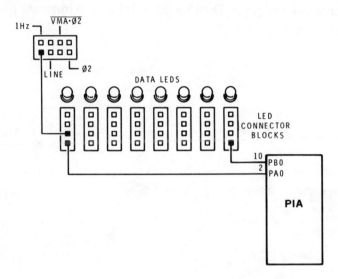

Figure 155
Display interface for serial data transfer.

8. Switch Trainer power on. Then enter the program listed in Figure 156. Do not attempt to enter data at address 0048_{16}. This address will serve as a temporary storage register.

    When this program is executed, data LED7 will flash on and off at approximately a 1 Hz rate. The 1 Hz signal will be used as a program timing signal through PIA pin PA0. The flashing LED will serve as a visual timing reference.

9. Execute the program. Data LED0 will light to indicate the program is running.

```
00001                           NAM     SERIAL01 REV 0.6
00002                           OPT     NOP
00003        8000    PIAIN      EQU     $8000
00004        FDF4    INCH       EQU     $FDF4
00005        8002    PIAOUT     EQU     $8002
00006 0000 CE FE04              LDX     #$FE04
00007 0003 FF 8000              STX     PIAIN
00008 0006 CE FF04              LDX     #$FF04
00009 0009 FF 8002              STX     PIAOUT
00010 000C 7F 0048              CLR     TEMP
00011 000F 73 8002              COM     PIAOUT
00012                 *GET HEX CHARACTER
00013 0012 BD FDF4 NXTCHR JSR   INCH
00014 0015 01                   NOP          *   8D    HOLD
00015 0016 01                   NOP          *   39    FOR
00016 0017 01                   NOP          *   8D    PROGRAM
00017 0018 01                   NOP          *   47    MODIFICATION
00018                 *COMMENCE WITH START BIT
00019 0019 7F 8002 RESET  CLR   PIAOUT   RESETS ALL OUT BITS
00020 001C 8D 1B              BSR   DELAY
00021                 *OUTPUT THE CHARACTER
00022 001E B7 8002            STA A PIAOUT   LSB IS STORED OUT
00023 0021 8D 16              BSR   DELAY
00024 0023 86 07              LDA A #07      NO. OF TIMES SHIFTED
00025 0025 76 8002 WORD  ROR   PIAOUT   NEXT MSB IS STORED OUT
00026 0028 8D 0F              BSR   DELAY
00027 002A 4A                 DEC A        *CHECK FOR NUMBER OF
00028 002B 26 F8              BNE   WORD     *BITS SHIFTED
00029                 *OUTPUT 2 STOP BITS
00030 002D 86 01              LDA A #$01     SET LSB
00031 002F B7 8002            STA A PIAOUT   STORE IT TO OUTPUT
00032 0032 8D 05  WAIT  BSR   DELAY
00033 0034 4A                 DEC A        *WAIT FOR TWO
00034 0035 26 FB              BNE   WAIT     *BIT TIMES
00035 0037 20 D9              BRA   NXTCHR   DONE! GET NEXT CHAR.
00036                 *DELAY SUBROUTINE
00037 0039 F6 8000 DELAY LDA B PIAIN    SAMPLE INPUT LOGIC LVL.
00038 003C 50                 NEG B        INPUT NOW FF OR 00
00039 003D F1 0048            CMP B TEMP     IS IT LIKE TEMP?
00040 0040 27 F7              BEQ   DELAY    IF SO, GET ANOTHER SAMPLE
00041 0042 73 0048            COM   TEMP     IF NOT, COMP TEMP
00042 0045 2B F2              BMI   DELAY    IF TEMP = FF, STAY IN LOOP
00043 0047 39                 RTS
00044 0048 0001  TEMP   RMB   1
00045                         END
```

Figure 156
Program to input serial data.

DISCUSSION

Until now, you have observed data words being displayed in a parallel manner only. That is, all of the bits contained in the data word or byte were displayed simultaneously. You will now display a data word *serially*. In the serial mode, data bits are displayed one after the other. For this experiment, the bits-per-second or baud rate will be very slow so that you will be able to recognize each data bit. Baud is defined as one bit per second.

When you return to the experiment, you will use the Trainer keyboard to enter a hex number. The number will be converted to its binary form and transferred to data LED 0 one bit at a time. However, what you will see is not a 4-bit word, but rather an 11-bit word.

When serial data is transferred, it must fulfill certain format conventions. These include a start bit, to indicate the beginning of a word; the information being transferred; and a stop bit, to indicate the end of a word. Depending on the instrument sending data, and the baud rate, the data word can have one start bit, six, seven, or eight data bits, zero or one parity bit (often considered one of the data bits) and one or two stop bits.

The word format used in this experiment uses one start bit, eight data bits, and two stop bits. Figure 157 illustrates the serial word for hex 5. For added clarity, the timing signal for data LED7 is included. Notice that the actual data is transferred, beginning with the LSB. Also, only the first four data bits (plus the start bit) are of interest, since you are only transferring a single hex digit. Later in the experiment, the remaining four data bits will be used.

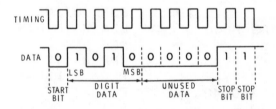

Figure 157
Serial data word format for the number
5_{16}.

PROCEDURE (Continued)

10. All timing is referenced to data LED7. Serial data is transferred through data LED0. When you are instructed to press a Trainer key, momentarily press the key while LED7 is **off**. It will take a little practice to be able to identify the data being transferred. Refer to Figure 157; it shows the data word you will observe when you press the 5 key. Press the 5 key and observe data LED's 0 and 7. Do it a number of times so that you can recognize each bit in the serial work.

11. Press a number of different Trainer keys and observe each serial word. You may find it helpful to illustrate each word, so you know what to expect.

DISCUSSION

Data direction register A is set so all of the pins of peripheral bus A are outputs, except for pin PA0. Thus, it will not be necessary to electrically tie the unused pins to a logic 1. Data direction register B is set so all of the pins of peripheral bus B are outputs. Then, temporary register 0048_{16} is cleared.

Since output register B contains logic 0's from PIA reset, the contents of the register are complemented. This turns data LED0 on, its waiting condition. Everything is now prepared, and the main program can begin.

The program immediately jumps to monitor routine INCH and waits for an input from the Trainer keyboard. When a key is pressed, PIA pin PB0 is cleared, generating a start bit. The delay used to set the bit time will be described at the end of the program.

After the start bit delay, the key number, now residing in accumulator A, is stored in output register B. Data LED0 immediately displays the LSB of the number. Then accumulator A is loaded with the number representing the number of times output register B must be rotated right in order to display each data bit in data LED0. The data in output register B is rotated through pin PB0 with a time delay after each rotate.

Once all eight data bits have been stored, 01_{16} is stored to output register B from the A accumulator. This forces LED0 on, indicating the first stop bit. After two time delays, for the two stop bits, the program branches back to monitor routine INCH and waits for a new key closure.

The delay subroutine uses the 1 Hz clock for timing. This is why the serial data transfer coincides with the lighting of data LED7.

At the beginning of the delay routine, PIA peripheral interface A is examined. Pin PA0 should be logic 0 if you pressed the Trainer key while LED7 was off (logic 0). Therefore, 00_{16} is stored in the B accumulator. (01_{16} would be stored if LED7 was on.)

The data in the B accumulator is negated and then compared with the temporary register (0048_{16}). Since both registers are equal, the program loops back and examines pin PA0 again. This cycle continues until pin PA0 goes to a logic 1. Accumulator B is loaded with 01_{16}. The data is negated to produce FF_{16}.

Since the B accumulator and temporary register are no longer equal, the temporary register is complemented. This changes its contents to FF_{16}, which represents a negative number to the MPU. Because the temporary register contains a negative number, the program branches back to the beginning of the delay routine.

Pin PA0 is again repeatedly examined for a logic level change from 1 to 0. When this level transition occurs, the program returns the temporary register to its orginal 00_{16} condition, and then returns the program counter to the main program. Thus, you have effectively generated a software one-shot monostable with a time period determined by the 1 Hz signal.

PROCEDURE (Continued)

12. Enter the program listed in Figure 158. Notice that the program begins at address 0050_{16}.

```
00001                          NAM     ASCICONV REV 0.1
00002                          OPT     NOP
00003  0050                    ORG     $50
00004                   *CONVERTS HEX TO ASCII
00005  0050  8A 30            ORA A   #$30        ASC NO. START WITH 3
00006  0052  81 39            CMP A   #$39        IS IT A NUMBER?
00007  0054  23 04            BLS     DONE        IF SO, DONE
00008  0056  80 09            SUB A   #$09        *LETTES START AT 1
00009  0058  8B 10            ADD A   #$10        *AND BEGIN WITH 4
00010  005A  39        DONE    RTS
00011                          END
```

Figure 158
Program to modify serial program for
ASCII word format.

13. Now return to address 0015_{16} and enter $8D_{16}$. Then enter 39_{16} at address 0016_{16}.

14. Execute the program beginning at address 0000_{16}. This is the beginning of the serial output program.

15. A hex to ASCII conversion subroutine has been added to the serial output program. Refer to Figure 159. Notice that ASCII representation for hex 5 is 35_{16}. Press the Trainer's 5 key and watch data LED0. Be sure to press the key while data LED7 is off. The serial data format remains unchanged, with one start bit, eight data bits, and two stop bits.

16. Press a number of Trainer keys, and observe the serial transfer for each key.

	COLUMN	0	1	2	3	4	5	6	7
ROW	BITS 765 4321	000	001	010	011	100	101	110	111
0	0000	NUL	DLE	SP	0	@	P	\	p
1	0001	SOH	DC1	!	1	A	Q	a	q
2	0010	STX	DC2	"	2	B	R	b	r
3	0011	ETX	DC3	#	3	C	S	c	s
4	0100	EOT	DC4	$	4	D	T	d	t
5	0101	ENQ	NAK	°₀	5	E	U	e	u
6	0110	ACK	SYN	&	6	F	V	f	v
7	0111	BEL	ETB	'	7	G	W	g	w
8	1000	BS	CAN	(	8	H	X	h	x
9	1001	HT	EM	)	9	I	Y	i	y
10	1010	LF	SUB	*	:	J	Z	j	z
11	1011	VT	ESC	-	:	K	[	k	{
12	1100	FF	FS	.	·	L	\	l	¦
13	1101	CR	GS	—		M	]	m	}
14	1110	SO	RS	.	.	N	⌒	n	~
15	1111	SI	US	⌠	?	O	—	o	DEL

Figure 159
Table of 7-bit American Standard
Code for information Interchange.

DISCUSSION

Remember that the Trainer outputs the hex value in binary when a number is pressed. Therefore, when the 5 key is pressed, 05_{16} will be loaded into the A accumulator, in the serial output program. Then the program will branch to the ASCII conversion routine. This is caused by the branch instruction in address 0015_{16} and the **relative** address for the branch in address 0016_{16}.

The first instruction in the conversion routine OR's 05_{16} with 30_{16} to produce 35_{16}. The next instruction compares 35_{16} with 39_{16}. If the first value is smaller (which it is) or equal to 39_{16}, a valid ASCII number is present in the A accumulator, and the program counter is sent back to the main program.

If a valid number is not present, 09_{16} is subtracted from the value in the A accumulator. Assume that the C key was pressed. Then the number stored in the A accumulator is $0C_{16}$. When OR'ed with 30_{16}, it equals $3C_{16}$. Remember that a compare instruction does not alter the contents of the accumulator. Therefore, when 09_{16} is subtracted from the contents of the A accumulator, the result is $3C_{16} - 09_{16} = 33_{16}$. Finally, 10_{16} is added to the contents of the A accumulator, resulting in the value 43_{16}. Notice in Figure 159 that 43_{16} equals C in ASCII code. Again the program counter returns to the main program.

PROCEDURE (Continued)

17. Enter the program listed in Figure 160. Notice that this program begins at address 0060_{16}. Stop after you enter 39_{16} at address 0075_{16}. Address 0076_{16} is used as a temporary register.

```
00001                         NAM      ADDPARIT REV 0.1
00002                         OPT      NOP
00003 0060                    ORG      $60
00004              *ADD PARITY BIT
00005 0060 7F 0076 PARITY CLR      PARIT1    START FRESH
00006 0063 C6 09          LDA B    #$09      TIMES TO SHIFT
00007 0065 49      BITCNT ROL A              SHIFT ONCE
00008 0066 24 03          BCC      NOINCR    SKIP INCR.
00009 0068 7C 0076        INC      PARIT1    COUNT LOGIC 1 BITS
00010 006B 5A      NOINCR DEC B              COUNT OFF TOTAL BITS
00011 006C 26 F7          BNE      BITCNT    ALL CHECKED YET?
00012 006E 76 0076        ROR      PARIT1    CHECK LSB OF PARIT1
00013 0071 24 02          BCC      FINIS     WAS IT ODD?
00014 0073 8A 80          ORA A    #$80      IF SO, SET PARITY BIT
00015 0075 39      FINIS  RTS
00016 0076 0001   PARIT1 RMB      1
00017                     END
```

Figure 160

Subroutine to add parity bit to serial output program.

18. Now return to address 0017_{16} and enter $8D_{16}$. Then enter 47_{16} at address 0018_{16}.

19. Execute the program beginning at address 0000_{16}. This is the beginning of the serial output program.

DISCUSSION

Remember from Unit 1 that a parity bit is added to a serial word as a data transfer check. It indicates whether the sum of logic 1's in the data portion of the word are odd or even. Thus, if you desire an **even** parity check, the sum of the parity bit and all of the other data bits must equal an even number. Odd parity requires that all of the data bits plus the parity bit equal an odd number.

For example, the ASCII code for the number 5 is 35_{16}. Since 35_{16} equals $0011\,0101_2$, the parity bit would be 0 for even parity and 1 for odd parity.

The parity bit occupies the eighth data bit position in the 8-bit data word. The first seven data bits contain the ASCII code.

PROCEDURE (Continued)

19. Determine the serial data word for hex 5. Then press the 5 key and observe LED0. Notice that the parity bit is 0 since the parity routine is configured for even parity.

20. Press a number of Trainer keys, and observe the serial transfer for each key.

21. Change the program data address 0071_{16} to 25_{16}. then press a number of Trainer keys, and observe the serial transfer for each key. The parity routine is now configured for odd parity.

DISCUSSION

After the hex number is converted to ASCII code, the program branches from address 0017_{16} to the "even" parity routine. This routine determines if a 1 or 0 will be placed in the eighth data bit to provide an even parity indication.

To begin, the temporary register at address 0076_{16} is cleared. This register will store the count of the number of logic 1 bits found in the data word. Accumulator B is loaded with 09_{16}, which will be decremented to monitor the bit count routine.

Accumulator A is rotated left and the carry bit is checked. If the carry is set, the temporary register is incremented; then the B accumulator is decremented. If the carry is clear, the B accumulator is immediately decremented. Since the B accumulator is not zero yet, the program loops back, and the process continues.

Notice that the A accumulator is rotated nine times. This is necessary since there are actually nine data bits including the carry bit, and the contents of this accumulator will be used by the main program. The carry bit will not affect the logic 1 bit count, since it was cleared by instruction $7F_{16}$.

After all of the bits in the A accumulator have been examined, and all 1's stored in the temporary register, the temporary register is rotated right. This places bit D_0 in the carry bit position. the carry bit is then examined. If it was clear, the program counter returns to the main program; the ASCII code contains an even number of 1's, and does not require modification. If the carry bit was set, accumulator A is OR'ed with 80_{16}, which places a 1 in the eighth (MSB) bit of the ASCII code. This makes the total number of 1's even in count. The program counter then returns to the main program.

To convert the parity bit routine to odd parity recognition, the code at address 0071_{16} is changed to 25_{16}. This causes a branch if the carry is set.

PROCEDURE (Continued)

22. Pull the circuit timing wire from the 1 Hz socket and connect it to the LINE socket.

23. Press a number of Trainer keys and observe the serial transfer at data LED0.

DISCUSSION

When you press each Trainer key, you can see data LED0 flash on and off at a rapid rate. This is because the baud rate is now equal to the line frequency. Although the transfer rate appears to be quite fast, it is considered very slow for computer work. Typical speeds for a teletypewriter are almost twice as fast as the line frequency. Speeds as high as 96.2 kilobaud are quite common.

PROCEDURE (Continued)

24. Do not disturb the circuit wired to your Trainer. It will be used in the next experiment. Proceed to Experiment 19.

Experiment 19

Digital-to-Analog and Analog-to-Digital Conversion

OBJECTIVES:

Show how to connect a digital-to-analog converter (DAC) to a microprocessor system.

Demonstrate how a DAC converts digital information into an analog equivalent.

Demonstrate a number of programs that will produce variable analog signal levels from a DAC.

Show how to convert a DAC into an analog-to-digital converter with a voltage comparator.

Demonstrate a program that implements the analog-to-digital conversion.

INTRODUCTION

When analog input and output capabilities are added to a microprocessor, its power can be greatly expanded. Basically, the microprocessor is a digital device that is ideal for control of discrete input/output levels. However, many analog signals can also be processed with a minimum of additional hardware. With this addition, such devices as temperature sensors and photo cells can be monitored, and analog signals can be coupled to various peripherals such as oscilloscopes and audio amplifiers.

In this experiment, you will learn how to use the digital-to-analog converter (DAC) for outputting an analog signal. You will also learn how to translate an analog signal into its equivalent digital value using the same DAC.

MATERIAL REQUIRED

1   ET-3400 Microprocessor Trainer with the PIA circuit wired to its large connector block

3   1000 ohm, 1/4-watt, 10% resistors

1   2000 ohm, 1/2-watt, 5% resistor

2   2700 ohm, 1/2-watt, 5% resistors

2   10k ohm, 1/2-watt, 5% resistors

1   1M ohm, 1/2-watt, 5% resistor

2   1000 ohm controls

1   47 pF ceramic capacitor

3   100 pF ceramic capacitors

1   1N4149 diode (56-56)

1   5.6-volt zener diode (56-616)

1   741 op amp integrated circuit (442-22)

1   301 op amp integrated circuit (442-39)

1   MC1406 DAC integrated circuit (443-842)

1   VOM, VTVM, or DVM with input impedance greater than 100 k ohm (11 M ohm desirable)

1   Oscilloscope (optional)

PROCEDURE

1. Switch the Trainer power off. Then remove the wires interconnecting LINE and data LED7, data LED7 and PIA pin 2, and data LED0 and PIA pin 10. The remaining PIA circuitry will be used in this experiment.

2. Refer to Figure 161 and construct the circuit shown, on the large connector block affixed to the Trainer cabinet. Be careful when you insert 1/2-watt resistor leads. It is easy to push a connector strip out of the bottom of the block. The 1000 ohm control leads will fit into the connector block if you straighten them out and then insert the control at a slight angle. You can also solder a short wire to each control lead. Figure 162 shows the complete PIA circuit with the DAC circuit added.

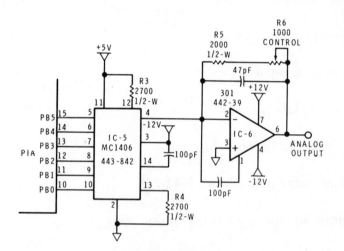

Figure 161
DAC circuit added to the PIA interface circuit.

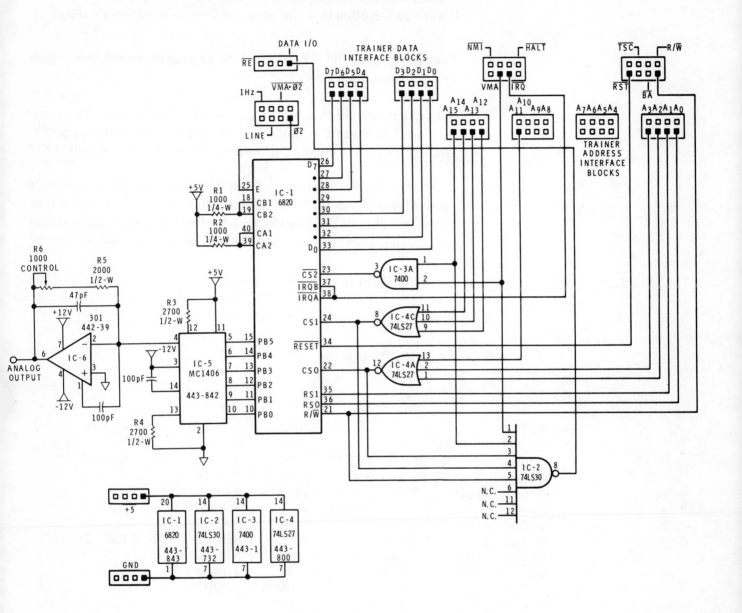

Figure 162

Circuit diagram fo the digital-to-
analog conversion circuit.

3. Switch the Trainer power on. Then enter the program listed in Figure 163. Notice that the program begins at address 0100_{16}.

4. Execute the program. Then, using the Trainer keyboard, press the 3 key and then the F key.

5. Set your voltmeter to measure 5 volts DC. Then connect the common lead to circuit ground, and the input lead to pin 6 of IC6 (analog output). You should measure approximately 0 volts DC.

6. Press 00 with the keyboard. Then adjust control R6 for a 5-volt output level. If you can not obtain a 5-volt level: switch the Trainer power off, change the value of resistor R5 from 2000 ohms to 1000 ohms, and then switch the Trainer power on again.

7. Press 20. What is the voltage level?_____

8. Press 30. What is the voltage level? _____

9. Press 10. What is the voltage level? _____

```
00001                          NAM    LINOUT    REV. 0.1
00002                          OPT    NOP
00003      FCBC    REDIS       EQU    $FCBC
00004      FE09    IHB         EQU    $FE09
00005 0100                     ORG    $0100
00006                     *CALIBRATION PROGRAM
00007 0100 CE FF04             LDX    #$FF04
00008 0103 FF 8002             STX    $8002      B SIDE IS OUT
00009 0106 BD FCBC NEWIN       JSR    REDIS
00010 0109 BD FE09             JSR    IHB
00011 010C B7 8002             STA A  $8002
00012 010F 20 F5               BRA    NEWIN
00013                          END
```

Figure 163
Program to convert digital values to their
analog equivalent.

DISCUSSION

The DAC converts a binary word into a proportional output current. This particular DAC is a 6-bit device. That means it can accomodate a 6-bit binary word. Therefore, the two most significant data bits from the PIA are not used.

This DAC requires a complemented input, that is, maximum current out occurs when the PIA output is 00_{16}. Minimum current occurs when all of the data lines are at a logic 1 level. This equals $3F_{16}$ (data bits PB6, PB7 not used).

Op amp IC6 (301) functions as a current-to-voltage converter. Feedback through resistor R5 and control R6 determines the gain of the op amp.

Since the DAC accomodates a 6-bit binary word, it is possible to have a conversion resolution of 2^6 or 64 discrete current levels. With IC6 calibrated for a voltage swing between 0 and 5 volts, each binary unit equals approximately 0.08 volts DC. Therefore, the approximate voltage levels you should have observed in steps 7, 8, and 9 are:

$$20_{16} = 2.44 \text{ VDC}$$

$$30_{16} = 1.16 \text{ VDC}$$

$$10_{16} = 3.72 \text{ VDC}$$

Refer to the program shown in Figure 163. The first two instructions set up the PIA so the B side operates as an output. REDIS then points to display H for data display. A second monitor routine, IHB, couples key closure data to the display, and also loads the data into the A accumulator. Two key entries are required to complete the monitor routine. The data is then stored to the PIA. Since only the first six data bits are used by the DAC, 00, 40, and $C0_{16}$ will convert to the same analog levels.

PROCEDURE (Continued)

10. Switch the Trainer power off. Then refer to Figure 164 and inter-connect the PIA and the binary data switches.

Figure 164

Peripheral data entry circuit for use with the digital-to-analog circuit.

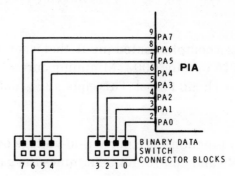

11. Switch the Trainer power on. Then enter the program listed in Figure 165. Notice that the program begins at address 0120_{16}.

12. Execute the program located at address 0120_{16}. Then set the binary data switches for $1F_{16}$. The voltmeter should indicate a slowly decreasing voltage that cyclically ramps from 5 volts to 0 volts.

13. The rate of voltage change is determined by the binary data switches. If you have an oscilloscope, connect its input to pin 6 of IC6 and circuit ground. Now change the binary data switches to 00_{16}. You should observe a descending voltage ramp.

```
00001                          NAM    OUTRAMP1 REV. 0.1
00002                          OPT    NOP
00003 0120                     ORG    $0120
00004 0120 CE 0004             LDX    #$0004
00005 0123 FF 8000             STX    $8000      A SIDE IN
00006 0126 CE FF04             LDX    #$FF04
00007 0129 FF 8002             STX    $8002      B SIDE OUT
00008 012C 4F                  CLR A
00009 012D B7 8002  NXTRMP     STA A  $8002
00010 0130 FE 8000             LDX    $8000      TIME TO WAIT
00011 0133 4C                  INC A             INCR RAMP STEP
00012 0134 09      STHOLD      DEX
00013 0135 26 FD               BNE    STHOLD
00014 0137 20 F4               BRA    NXTRMP
00015                          END
```

Figure 165

Program to generate a voltage ramp.

DISCUSSION

The voltage ramp in this program is a composite of 64 discrete voltage steps. Each step represents a binary value. Therefore, an 8-bit DAC would have produced a ramp with 256 discrete steps, while a 4-bit DAC would contain only 16 steps.

PROCEDURE (Continued)

14. Change the data at address 0133_{16} to $4A_{16}$. Then execute the program. You should observe an ascending voltage ramp. If you only have a voltmeter, change the binary data switches to $1F_{16}$. This will slow the ramp rate so you can observe the voltage change.

DISCUSSION

The ramp program sets the A side of the PIA as an input, and the B side as an output. The A accumulator is cleared so the ramp will begin at +5 volts. Accumulator A is stored to the DAC through the PIA. Then the index register is loaded with the binary switch data. This will determine the waiting period between voltage ramp steps.

Remember that the index register always contains two bytes of data. The first byte (high byte) is obtained from the specified address, and the second byte (low byte) is obtained from the specified address plus one. Therefore, when you load the index register from the PIA, the high byte contains the binary switch data, and the low byte contains 04_{16}. 04_{16} is the data stored in the A side control register of the PIA during initialization.

Accumulator A is incremented for the next voltage level, and the index register is decremented until it reaches 0000_{16}. Then the program branches back to store the A accumulator, and the cycle continues. It is not necessary to clear accumulator A once the voltage ramp reaches zero, since the next increment sets the six least significant binary data bits to zero.

PROCEDURE (Continued)

15. Enter the program listed in Figure 166. Notice that this program begins at address 0140_{16}.

16. Execute the program beginning at address 0140_{16}. Set the binary data switches to $1F_{16}$. The voltage should step from 0 to 5 volts and then back to 0 volts in a cyclic manner. You can observe this dual ramp (triangle) waveform on the oscilloscope, if you increase the ramp rate with the binary data switches.

```
00001                              NAM    TRIANGLE REV. 0.1
00002                              OPT    NOP
00003 0140                         ORG    $0140
00004 0140 CE 0004                 LDX    #$0004
00005 0143 FF 8000                 STX    $8000      A SIDE IN
00006 0146 CE FF04                 LDX    #$FF04
00007 0149 FF 8002                 STX    $8002      B SIDE OUT
00008 014C 86 3F                   LDA A  #$3F        DAC OUT = 0
00009 014E FE 8000    UP           LDX    $8000      DELAY TIME
00010 0151 B7 8002                 STA A  $8002      OUT TO DAC
00011 0154 27 10                   BEQ    DOWN1
00012 0156 4A         UP1          DEC A
00013 0157 09         LOOP1        DEX
00014 0158 26 FD                   BNE    LOOP1
00015 015A 20 F2                   BRA    UP
00016 015C FE 8000    DOWN         LDX    $8000      DELAY TIME
00017 015F B7 8002                 STA A  $8002      OUT TO DAC
00018 0162 81 3F                   CMP A  #$3F
00019 0164 27 F0                   BEQ    UP1
00020 0166 4C         DOWN1        INC A
00021 0167 09         LOOP2        DEX
00022 0168 26 FD                   BNE    LOOP2
00023 016A 20 F0                   BRA    DOWN
00024                              END
```

Figure 166
Program to generate a triangle waveform.

DISCUSSION

This program uses the A side of the PIA to enter step delay data and the B side to output the discrete voltage level data. However, this time the A accumulator is loaded with $3F_{16}$, which is the binary equivalent of 0 volts.

Beginning at address $014E_{16}$, the index register is loaded with the level step delay time. Then the A accumulator is stored to the PIA. If accumulator A is zero, the program branches to address 0166_{16}. Since it equals $3F_{16}$, the A accumulator is decremented. Then, the index register is decremented until it equals 0000_{16}.

At the end of delay, the index register is again loaded, and the contents of the A accumulator are stored to the PIA. This cycle continues until the A accumulator equals 00_{16} (5-volt level). Then the program branches to address 0166_{16}.

Addresses 015C through $016B_{16}$ are similar to the first part of the program. They differ in that the A accumulator is incremented and compared to $0F_{16}$. Thus, the voltage level is cycled from 0 to 5 volts in the UP program section, and from 5 to 0 volts in the DOWN program section.

PROCEDURE (Continued)

17. Enter the program listed in Figure 167. Notice that this program begins at address 0000_{16}.

18. Execute the program. This program produces a sine waveform at a fixed frequency of about 200 Hz. If you only have a voltmeter, it should indicate approximately 1.7 volts AC. An oscilloscope will show a slightly distorted waveform. This is because of the resolution provided by the 6-bit DAC. An 8-bit DAC would produce a more symmetrical waveform.

```
00001                           NAM    SINEWAVE REV.0.2
00002                           OPT    NOP
00003  0000  CE FF04            LDX    #$FF04
00004  0003  FF 8002            STX    $8002
00005  0006  CE 003B            LDX    #BTABLE
00006  0009  C6 11     SIN1     LDA B  #$11
00007  000B  A6 00     SIN1A    LDA A  X
00008  000D  01                 NOP
00009  000E  B7 8002            STA A  $8002
00010  0011  08                 INX
00011  0012  5A                 DEC B
00012  0013  26 F6              BNE    SIN1A
00013  0015  C6 11     SIN2     LDA B  #$11
00014  0017  A6 00     SIN2A    LDA A  X
00015  0019  01                 NOP
00016  001A  B7 8002            STA A  $8002
00017  001D  09                 DEX
00018  001E  5A                 DEC B
00019  001F  26 F6              BNE    SIN2A
00020  0021  C6 11     SIN3     LDA B  #$11
00021  0023  A6 00     SIN3A    LDA A  X
00022  0025  43                 COM A
00023  0026  B7 8002            STA A  $8002
00024  0029  08                 INX
00025  002A  5A                 DEC B
00026  002B  26 F6              BNE    SIN3A
00027  002D  C6 11     SIN4     LDA B  #$11
00028  002F  A6 00     SIN4A    LDA A  X
00029  0031  43                 COM A
00030  0032  B7 8002            STA A  $8002
00031  0035  09                 DEX
00032  0036  5A                 DEC B
00033  0037  26 F6              BNE    SIN4A
00034  0039  20 CE              BRA    SIN1
00035  003B  20        BTABLE   FCB    $20,$22,$25,$27,$2A,$2D,$2F
       003C  22
       003D  25
       003E  27
       003F  2A
       0040  2D
       0041  2F
00036  0042  31                 FCB    $31,$33,$35,$37,$39,$3A,$3B
       0043  33
       0044  35
       0045  37
       0046  39
       0047  3A
       0048  3B
00037  0049  3C                 FCB    $3C,$3D,$3E,$3E
       004A  3D
       004B  3E
       004C  3E
00038                           END
```

Figure 167

Program to generate a sine waveform.

DISCUSSION

The program uses a "look-up" table (addresses 003B through $004C_{16}$) of constant values to generate a sine wave signal. The table was produced by deriving the sine of the angles between 0° and 90° in 5° increments, and then multiplying each value by a constant.

Because the sine wave must reside within a 0 to 5-volt "window," each 90° segment of the waveform can only be generated by 32 of the possible data bits. The first 90° of the sine wave starts at approximately 2.5 volts and steps to 0 volts. The second 90° steps from 0 volts up to 2.5 volts. The third 90° steps from 2.5 volts up to 5 volts. Finally, the fourth 90° steps from 5 volts down to 2.5 volts.

With the program using only 32 data levels for each waveform segment, the first five data bits in each byte determine the digital voltage level, while the sixth bit (D_5) determines whether the lower two waveform segments or the upper two waveform segments are being generated. Refer to the program in Figure 167. Notice that the table of values begins at 20_{16}, which approximately equals 2.5 volts. The values increase (voltage decrease) from there. When the upper half of the sine waveform is produced, the table values are complemented to generate the voltages between 2.5 and 5 volts.

In the program, the first two steps initialize the PIA. Then, the index register is loaded with the address of the first value in the look-up table. Accumulator B is loaded with 11_{16}, which will be decremented to show when all of the table values have been used.

The next six instructions form a "fetch and display" loop that generates the first waveform segment. Accumulator A is loaded with the first value (20_{16}). The NOP occupies time to make the loop time identical to the time used when the third and fourth segments are generated. Accumulator A is stored to the PIA. The index register is incremented, to point to the next value in the table, and the B accumulator is decremented. Since the register is not zero, the program branches back to address $000B_{16}$. This continues until the B accumulator equals 00_{16}.

Then, the B accumulator is loaded with 11_{16}. Remember that the index register contains the address of the last value in the table $(004C_{16})$. The next six instructions form another fetch and display loop to generate the second waveform segment. The only instruction that differs from the first loop is "decrement the index register" rather than increment.

After the loop is completed, the B accumulator is loaded with 11_{16}. The index register now contains the address $(003B_{16})$ of the value at the top of the table. The next six instructions form the third fetch and display loop. This is identical to the first program loop; except, the NOP instruction is replaced with a "complement the A accumulator" instruction. Thus, the table values can now be used to generate the upper half of the sine waveform. Program loop four also operates in this manner.

PROCEDURE (Continued)

19. Switch the Trainer power off. Then remove the eight wires interconnecting the binary data switches and the PIA.

20. Refer to Figure 168 and add the new circuit shown to the DAC circuit. The output of the new circuit is connected to pin 9 (PA7) of the PIA. If you changed the value of R5 (in the DAC circuit) to 1000 ohms, in a previous section of this experiment, remove the 1000 ohm resistor and reinstall the 2000 ohm, 1/2-watt resistor in its place.

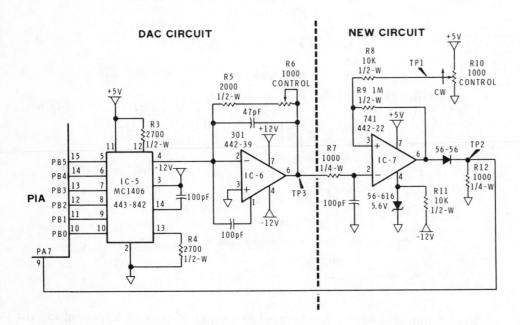

Figure 168
New circuit adds a voltage comparator to
produce an analog-to-digital converter.

21. Switch the Trainer power on. Then, enter the program listed in Figure 169. Notice that the program begins at address 0170_{16}.

22. Turn control R10 fully clockwise, then execute the program beginning at address 0170_{16}.

```
00001                         NAM    A-TO-D    REV.0.1
00002                         OPT    NOP
00003 0170                    ORG    $0170
00004      FCBC     REDIS     EQU    $FCBC
00005      FE20     OUTBYT    EQU    $FE20
00006                     *INITIALIZE PIA
00007 0170 CE 0004           LDX    #$0004
00008 0173 FF 8000           STX    $8000       A SIDE IN
00009 0176 CE FF04           LDX    #$FF04
00010 0179 FF 8002           STX    $8002       B SIDE OUT
00011                     *FIND EQUAL POINT
00012 017C C6 FF   NEWIN     LDA B  #$FF        FF=LOW VOLTAGE
00013 017E 4F                CLR A
00014 017F F7 8002 NXTSTP    STA B  $8002
00015 0182 CE 0055           LDX    #$0055      *
00016 0185 09      WAIT      DEX                *HARDWARE SETTLE WAIT
00017 0186 26 FD             BNE    WAIT        *
00018 0188 7D 8000           TST    $8000       CHECK COMPARITOR
00019 018B 2A 06             BPL    FOUND
00020 018D 5A                DEC B
00021 018E 8B 01             ADD A  #01
00022 0190 19                DAA
00023 0191 20 EC             BRA    NXTSTP
00024                     *OUTPUT RESULTS
00025 0193 BD FCBC FOUND     JSR    REDIS       SET DISPLAY LOCATION
00026 0196 BD FE20           JSR    OUTBYT      OUTPUT BYTE
00027 0199 86 01             LDA A  #01         *  TURN ON
00028 019B B7 C16F           STA A  $C16F
00029 019E 20 DC             BRA    NEWIN       *  DECIMAL POINT
00030                         END
```

Figure 169

Program to convert an analog signal to a
digital value.

23. Connect your voltmeter to TP1 (wiper of control R10) and circuit ground. Then, adjust control R6 for a Trainer display equal in value to the voltage at TP1. If you cannot adjust the display value down to the indicated voltage level, place a 1000 ohm, 1/4-watt resistor in series with resistor R5. Make sure you switch the Trainer power off before you add the resistor.

24. The circuit you have constructed acts like a digital voltmeter and will measure the voltage at the wiper of control R10 (TP1). Turn control R10 and compare the voltage indicated by your voltmeter with the voltage indicated by the Trainer display.

DISCUSSION

In this analog-to-digital conversion circuit, the MPU supplies a known voltage to a voltage comparator, and looks for a match with the unknown voltage at the comparator. Because the program operates in digit increments, each voltage level step will equal 0.1 volts after the circuit has been calibrated. Thus, the unknown voltage can be resolved to one-tenth of a volt.

At the beginning of the program, the PIA is initialized (A side in, B side out); the B accumulator is loaded with FF (to start comparison at 0 volts); and the A accumulator is cleared (used to store the voltage count, for the display). The B accumulator is stored to the PIA for conversion to a voltage level. The next three instructions use the index register to supply a short time delay. This is needed since the analog circuit cannot operate as quickly as the MPU.

After the short delay, the comparator output to the A side of the PIA is checked for a voltage match. If there is no match, the B accumulator is decremented, increasing the voltage level, and the A accumulator is incremented, by adding 01_{16} to the contents, to indicate the voltage increase. Since this circuit is emulating a digital voltmeter, the displayed voltage must be in decimal (base 10). Therefore, the next instruction performs a decimal adjust on the A accumulator. This converts the binary addition to a BCD format.

The program then branches back to address $017F_{16}$ and repeats until the comparator test indicates that the voltage generated by the MPU equals the unknown voltage. You can observe the conversion routine by connecting the Y1 input of a dual-trace oscilloscope to TP2 and circuit ground, and the Y2 input to TP3 and circuit ground. Figure 167 shows the location of the test points, while Figure 170 shows the display of the 0.5-volt conversion.

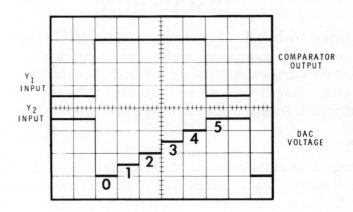

Figure 170
Voltage comparator timing in relation to
the DAC voltage signal.

As soon as the comparator senses that the known and unknown voltages are equal, it switches low to tell the MPU a match has occurred. This causes the program to branch to the display output routine. REDIS stores the location of display H. OUTBYT writes the contents of the A accumulator to displays H and I. Next, the contents of the A accumulator is changed to 01_{16}. This is stored to address $C16F_{16}$, which lights the decimal point in display H.

PROCEDURE (Continued)

25.   Switch the Trainer power off. Then remove the wires and components from the two large connector blocks. Caution: The PIA is an MOS device. When you remove it from the Trainer, press it onto its conductive foam pad. This will reduce the possibility of damage from static electricity.

MIC

NOTES:

1. ALL RESISTORS ARE 1/4 WATT, 10% UNLESS MARKED OTHERWISE. RESISTOR VALUES ARE IN OHMS (k=1000; M=1,000,000).

2. ALL CAPACITORS ARE IN µF UNLESS MARKED OTHERWISE.

3. THIS SYMBOL INDICATES A DC VOLTAGE TAKEN WITH A HIGH IMPEDANCE INPUT VOLTMETER, FROM THE POINT INDICATED TO CHASSIS GROUND. VOLTAGES MAY VARY ±20%.

4. THIS SYMBOL INDICATES CIRCUIT BOARD GROUND.

5. THIS SYMBOL INDICATES A CONNECTOR IN A CONNECTOR BLOCK.

6. FUSE IS CRITICAL FOR CONTINUED SAFETY. REPLACE THEM ONLY WITH PARTS OF THE SAME RATING OR WITH THE PROPER HEATH PARTS.

7. IF YOU INSTALL THE 40-PIN ACCESSORY CONNECTOR, CONNECTIONS ARE TO THE BUFFERED LINES (□) USE JUMPER WIRES TO CONNECT THE DATA LINES.

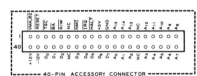

40-PIN ACCESSORY CONNECTOR

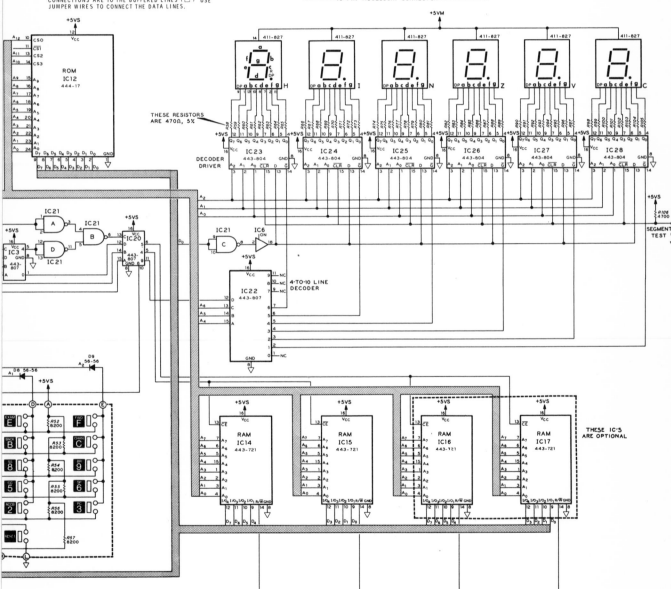

EXAMINATIONS

Unit 1 Examination

Number Systems and Codes

This examination will test your knowledge of the important facts in Unit 1. It will tell you what you have learned and what you need to review. Answer all questions first; then check your work against the correct answers given later.

1. Indicate the base or radix of the following number systems.

    A. Octal _____.
    B. Decimal _____.
    C. Hexadecimal _____.
    D. Binary _____.

2. Write the following numbers using positional notation.

    A. 1101.011_2
    B. 1010.01_{10}
    C. 1001.101_8.
    D. 1110.11_{16}

3. Convert the following numbers to decimal.

    A. 10011.011_2
    B. 752.31_8
    C. $A8C.5F_{16}$

4. Convert the following numbers to binary.

    A. 105.0625_{10}
    B. 374.24_8
    C. $F19.6C_{16}$

5. Convert the following numbers to octal.

    A. 638.3125_{10}
    B. 10010101.0110101_2

6.   Convert the following numbers to hexadecimal.

     A. 9587.03125_{10}
     B. $1101101101010.101110101_2$

7.   The ASCII and BAUDOT codes are a form of _____
     _____ codes.

8.   Convert the following numbers to 8421 BCD code.

     A. 521.372_{10}
     B. 1010.011_2

9.   Convert the 8421 BCD code 1001 0101.0111 0011 to decimal.

10. Convert the 8421 BCD code 0101 0011.0111 0101 to binary.

11. Which type of parity is used when the 8-bit ASCII character
     01110111 is transmitted?

     A. Odd
     B. Even

12. The BAUDOT code uses _____ bit numbers to generate a
     character.

13. Using only your knowledge of binary codes, identify the Gray code.

Decimal	a	b	c	d
0	0000	0000	0000	0011
1	0001	0001	0001	0100
2	0011	0010	0010	0101
3	0010	0011	0011	0110
4	0110	0100	0100	0111
5	0111	0101	1011	1000
6	0101	0110	1100	1001
7	0100	0111	1101	1010
8	1100	1000	1110	1011
9	1101	1001	1111	1100

Unit 2 Examination

Microcomputer Basics

1.   In microprocessor terminology, the number or piece of data that is operated upon is called the:

A.   Operand.
B.   Opcode.
C.   Address.
D.   Instruction.

2.   The part of the instruction that tells the microprocessor what operation to perform is called the:

A.   Operand.
B.   Opcode.
C.   Address.
D.   Mnemonic.

3.   The portion of the microcomputer in which instructions and data are stored is called the:

A.   ALU.
B.   MPU.
C.   RAM.
D.   Data bus.

4.   An 8-bit byte in memory can represent an:

A.   Opcode.
B.   Operand.
C.   Address.
D.   All of the above.

5.   During the fetch phase:

A.   The opcode is fetched from memory and is decoded.
B.   The address of the operand is fetched from memory and is decoded.
C.   The operand is fetched from memory and is operated upon.
D.   The program count is fetched from memory.

6. In what register is the result of an arithmetic operation normally placed?

   A. The data register.
   B. The address register.
   C. The arithmetic logic unit (ALU).
   D. The accumulator.

7. During the fetch and execute phases of the "load accumulator direct" instruction, the information on the data bus will be:

   A. The operand address followed by the operand.
   B. The program count, followed by the opcode, followed by the operand address, followed by the operand.
   C. The opcode, followed by the operand address, followed by the operand.
   D. The opcode, followed by the operand.

8. In the immediate addressing mode, the second byte of the instruction is the:

   A. Opcode of the instruction.
   B. Number that is to be operated upon.
   C. Address of the operand.
   D. Address of the opcode.

9. In the direct addressing mode, the second byte of the instruction is the:

   A. Opcode of the instruction.
   B. Number that is to be operated upon.
   C. Address of the operand.
   D. Address of the opcode.

10. Which of the following is normally a one-byte instruction?

    A. Halt.
    B. Add immediate.
    C. Load accumulator direct.
    D. Store accumulator direct.

11.   At the start of the fetch phase, the program counter contains:

A.   The address of the operand to be fetched.
B.   The address of the opcode to be fetched.
C.   The opcode of the instruction.
D.   The operand.

12.   Which register holds the opcode while it is being decoded?

A.   The address register.
B.   The accumulator.
C.   The data register.
D.   The program counter.

13.   The program shown in Figure 171 below:

A.   Adds the contents of memory location 09, 0A, and 0B.
B.   Stores 00 in locations 09, 0A, 0B.
C.   Stores 09 in location 03, 0A in location 05, and 0B in location 07.
D.   Stores 0B in the accumulator.

HEX ADDRESS	HEX CONTENTS	MNEMONICS/ CONTENTS
00	86	LDA
01	00	00_{16}
02	97	STA
03	09	09_{16}
04	97	STA
05	0A	$0A_{16}$
06	97	STA
07	0B	$0B_{16}$
08	3E	HLT
09	—	—
0A	—	—
0B	—	—

Figure 171
Program for Question 13.

14. The program shown in Figure 172:

    A. Multiplies 4 times 4 and holds the product in the accumulator.
    B. Multiplies 9 times 3 and holds the product in the accumulator.
    C. Multiplies 4 times 3 and stores the product in the accumulator.
    D. Multiplies 9 times 4 and holds the product in the accumulator.

Figure 172

Program for Question 14.

HEX ADDRESS	HEX CONTENTS	MNEMONICS/ CONTENTS
00	96	LDA
01	09	09_{16}
02	9B	ADD
03	09	09_{16}
04	9B	ADD
05	09	09_{16}
06	9B	ADD
07	09	09_{16}
08	3E	HLT
09	04	04_{16}

15. The program shown in Figure 173:

    A. Swaps the contents of memory location 0D and 0E.
    B. Stores AA_{16} in locations 0D, 0E, and 0F.
    C. Stores BB_{16} in locations 0D, 0E, and 0F.
    D. Adds AA and BB, storing the sum at location 0F.

Figure 173

Program for Question 15.

HEX ADDRESS	HEX CONTENTS	MNEMONICS/ CONTENTS
00	96	LDA
01	0D	$0D_{16}$
02	97	STA
03	0F	$0F_{16}$
04	96	LDA
05	0E	$0E_{16}$
06	97	STA
07	0D	$0D_{16}$
08	96	LDA
09	0F	$0F_{16}$
0A	97	STA
0B	0E	$0E_{16}$
0C	3E	HLT
0D	AA	AA_{16}
0E	BB	BB_{16}
0F	—	—

Unit 3 Examination

Computer Arithmetic

1. Add 10010110_2 to 1101_2.

2. Subtract 1011_2 from 10110110_2.

3. Multiply 1001_2 by 1100_2.

4. Divide 100111_2 with 110_2.

5. The 1's complement of 00110110_2 is _____.

6. The 2's complement of 00110110_2 is _____.

7. Using 2's complement arithmetic, add $+75_{10}$ to -6_{10}.

8. Using 2's complement arithmetic, add -35_{10} to -75_{10}.

9. Using 2's complement arithmetic, subtract -15_{10} from -85_{10}.

10. The truth table Figure 174 represents the logical _____ function.

INPUT		OUTPUT
A	B	C
0	0	0
1	0	1
0	1	1
1	1	0

Figure 174
Truth Table for Exam Question 10.

11. Logically AND 11011010 with 10010110.

12. Logically OR 11011010 with 10010110.

13. Logically EOR 11011010 with 10010110.

14. Logically invert 11011010.

Unit 4 Examination

Introduction to Programming

1.   The BRA instruction will cause a branch to occur:

    A.   Anytime that it is executed.
    B.   Only if the Z flag is set.
    C.   Only if the N flag is set.
    D.   Only if the C flag is set.

2.   The address that follows the opcode of an unconditional branch instruction is:

    A.   The address of the operand.
    B.   The address of the next opcode to be executed.
    C.   Added to the program count to form the address of the next opcode to be executed.
    D.   Added to the program count to form the address of the operand that is to be tested to see if a branch operation is required.

3.   The opcode for an unconditional branch instruction is at address AF_{16}. The relative address is $0F_{16}$. From what address will the next opcode be fetched?

    A. $A0_{16}$.
    B. $C0_{16}$.
    C. BE_{16}.
    D. $B1_{16}$.

4.   The opcode for an unconditional branch instruction is at address 30_{16}. The relative address is EF_{16}. From what address will the next opcode be fetched?

    A. 21_{16}.
    B. EF_{16}.
    C. 32_{16}.
    D. 19_{16}.

5.   The carry register:

    A.   Acts like the ninth bit of the accumulator.
    B.   Is set when a "borrow" for bit 7 of the accumulator occurs.
    C.   Is set when a carry from bit 7 occurs.
    D.   All the above.

6. The numbers 0101 1000$_2$ and 0110   0011$_2$ are added using the ADD instruction. Immediately after the ADD instruction is executed, the condition code registers will indicate the following:

   A. C=1, N=1, V=1, Z=0.
   B. C=0, N=1, V=1, Z=0.
   C. C=0, N=0, V=1, Z=1.
   D. C=0, N=0, V=1, Z=1.

7. The divide program shown in Figure 4-16 of the text works only if the dividend is initially less than + 128$_{10}$. The program can be modified to work for dividends up to 255$_{10}$ by replacing the BMI instruction with the:

   A. BEQ instruction.
   B. BNE instruction.
   C. BCC instruction.
   D. BCS instruction.

8. A binary number can be converted to BCD by repeatedly:

   A. Dividing by powers of two.
   B. Subtracting powers of ten.
   C. Multiplying by powers of two.
   D. Adding powers of ten.

9. The DAA instruction is used:

   A. To convert a binary number to BCD.
   B. To convert a BCD number to binary.
   C. After an add instruction to adjust the sum to a BCD number.
   D. After a subtract instruction to adjust the difference to a BCD number.

10. When you are adding multiple-precision binary numbers, all bytes except the least significant ones must be:

   A. Added using the ADD instruction.
   B. Added using the DAA instruction.
   C. Added using the ADC instruction.
   D. Decimal adjusted before addition takes place.

Unit 5 Examination

The 6800 Microprocessor — Part 1

1. Which of the following program segments will **not** clear both accumulators?

   A. CLRA
      CLRB

   B. CLRA
      TAB

   C. CLRB
      TBA

   D. CLRA
      ABA

2. Which of the following contains an operation that can **not** be performed directly on a byte in memory using a single instruction?

   A. Increment, decrement, shift left arithmetically.
   B. Clear, complement, compare.
   C. Rotate left, negate, test for zero.
   D. Shift right logically, rotate right, test for minus.

3. Which addressing mode is best suited for adding a list of numbers?

   A. Direct.
   B. Extended.
   C. Indexed.
   D. Relative.

4. Which of the following program segments will sucessfully swap the contents of accumulators A and B?

   A. TAB
      TBA

   C. TAB
      ABA

   B. STAA
      10
      TBA
      LDAB
      10

   D. STAA
      10
      LDAB
      10
      TBA

5. Which of the following program segments will cause a branch if the number in memory location 8310 is odd?

   A. ROR
      83
      10
      BCS
      07

   C. RORA
      BCS
      07

   B. ASL
      83
      10
      BCS
      07

   D. LDAA
      83
      10
      ROLA
      BCS
      07

6. Examine the following program segment:

```
        CLRA
     ┌─ INCA
     │  BNE
     └─ FD
        WAI
```

If an MPU cycle is 1 microsecond, how much time elapses from the time this segment starts running until the WAI instruction is fetched?

A. Approximately 8 microseconds.
B. Approximately 2050 microseconds.
C. Approximately 1538 microseconds.
D. Approximately 3 microseconds.

7. Which of the following instructions can be used to clear the Z flag?

   A. BEQ
   B. BNE
   C. NOP
   D. TAP

8. Which of the following instructions can be used to test the result of the subtraction of unsigned binary numbers?

   A. BGE.
   B. BGT.
   C. BCS.
   D. BLT

9. Examine the following program segment:

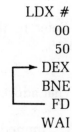

```
        LDX #
          00
          50
        DEX
        BNE
        FD
        WAI
```

How many times will the DEX instruction be executed?

   A. Once
   B. 50_{16} times.
   C. $65,536_{10}$.
   D. The number of times will depend on the contents of memory location 0050.

HEX ADDRESS	HEX CONTENTS	MNEMONICS/ HEX CONTENTS	COMMENTS
0010	4F	CLRA	Clear Accumulator A.
0011	7D	TST	Test
0012	00	00	the
0013	1E	1E	multiplier.
0014	27	BEQ	If it is zero branch to wait.
0015	07	07	
0016	7A	DEC	Otherwise decrement
0017	00	00	the
0018	1E	1E	multiplier.
0019	9B	ADDA	Add the
001A	1F	1F	multiplicand to the product.
001B	20	BRA	Repeat the loop.
001C	F4	F4	
001D	3E	WAI	Wait.
001E	05	Multiplier	
001F	04	Multiplicand	

Figure 175

This program multiplies by repeated addition.

NOTE: Refer to the program shown in Figure 175 for questions 10 through 16.

10. What addressing mode does the TST instruction use?

   A. Immediate
   B. Direct.
   C. Extended.
   D. Indexed.

11. The BEQ instruction checks to see if the TST instruction set the:

   A. Z flag
   B. C flag.
   C. H flag.
   D. V flag.

12. The DEC instruction decrements the number in:

   A. Accumulator A.
   B. Memory location 001E.
   C. Accumulator B.
   D. The index register.

13. Which instruction is executed immediately after the BRA instruction?

   A. WAI.
   B. BEQ.
   C. CLRA.
   D. TST.

14. With the values given for the multiplier and multiplicand, how many times will the main program loop be repeated?

   A. Four times.
   B. Five times.
   C. Twenty times.
   D. Twice.

15. After the program has been executed, memory location 001E will contain:

   A. 05_{16}.
   B. 04_{16}.
   C. 20_{16}.
   D. 00_{16}.

16. After the program has been executed, the product will appear in:

   A. Memory location 001E.
   B. Memory location 001F.
   C. Accumulator A.
   D. Accumulator B.

HEX ADDRESS	HEX CONTENTS	MNEMONICS/ HEX CONTENTS	COMMENTS
0010	CE	LDX #	
0011	00	00	
0012	00	05	
0013	A6	LDAA, X	
0014	20	20	
0015	AB	ADDA, X	
0016	30	30	
0017	A7	STAA, X	
0018	40	40	
0019	08	INX	
001A	8C	CPX #	
001B	00	00	
001C	15	15	
001D	26	BNE	
001E	F4	F4	
001F	3E	WAI	

Figure 176

Program for Questions 17 through 20.

NOTE: Refer to Figure 176 for Questions 17 through 20. Analyze the program, determine what it does, and fill in appropriate comments.

17. On the first pass through the main program loop, the LDAA, X instruction takes its operand from memory location:

A. 0005.

B. 0020.

C. 0025.

D. 0014.

18. On the first pass, the ADDA, X adds the contents of what memory location to accumulator A?

    A.   0005.
    B.   0030.
    C.   0035.
    D.   0016.

19. On the second pass through the program loop, the contents of memory location:

    A.   0021 are added to the contents of 0031 and the result is stored in 0041.
    B.   0026 are added to the contents of 0036 and the result is stored in 0046.
    C.   0025 are added to the contents of 0035 and the result is stored in 0045.
    D.   0020 are added to the contents of 0030 and the result is stored in 0040.

20. How many times is the main program loop repeated?

    A. 10_{16} times.
    B. 05_{16} times.
    C. 30_{16} times.
    D. 15_{16} times.

Unit 6 Examination

The 6800 Microprocessor — Part 2

1. If the I bit in the condition code register is set, the MPU will ignore:
   A. The reset signal.
   B. The non-maskable interrupt signal.
   C. The interrupt request signal.
   D. The software interrupt instruction.

2. Which of the following lists contains instructions that do **not** change the contents of the stack pointer?
   A. PULA, DES, RTI, WAI.
   B. PSHB, INS, RTS, SWI.
   C. TXS, BSR, PULB, LDS.
   D. PSHA, JMP, TSX, STS.

3. Which of the following program segments will successfully swap the contents of the two accumulators?

A.	PSHA	B.	PSHB	C.	PSHA	D.	PSHB
	TAB		TAB		TBA		TBA
	PULA		PULA		PULA		PULB

4. The stack pointer is automatically:
   A. Decremented before data is pushed onto the stack.
   B. Incremented before data is pushed onto the stack.
   C. Decremented after data is pushed onto the stack.
   D. Incremented after data is pushed onto the stack.

5. One difference between the JMP and JSR instruction is:
   A. JMP can use either extended or indexed addressing.
   B. The program count is saved when JSR is executed.
   C. The JSR will be executed even if the interrupt mask is set.
   D. JMP is an unconditional jump.

6. The last instruction in a subroutine is generally:
   A. A JMP instruction.
   B. An RTS instruction.
   C. An RTI instruction.
   D. A JSR instruction.

7. In the 6800 MPU, which of the following instructions could be used to transfer data from an I/O device to accumulator A?
   A. INPA.
   B. LDAA.
   C. STAA.
   D. OUTA.

8. Refer to Figures 6-17 and 6-18. Which of the following program segments will read in data from the switch bank and, if the number is larger than $2A_{16}$, display it on the LED's?

A. LDAA	B. LDAA	C. LDAA	D. LDAA
80	80	80	90
00	00	00	00
CMPA#	SUBA#	STAA	SUBA#
2A	2A	90	2A
BHI	BHI	00	BHI
01	01		01
WAI	WAI		WAI
STAA	STAA		STA
90	90		80
00	00		00

9. Which of the following types of interrupts does **not** cause data to be pushed into the stack?
   A. Software interrupt.
   B. Non-maskable interrupt.
   C. Reset interrupt.
   D. Interrupt request.

10. Generally, the last instruction in an interrupt service routine will be:
   A. An RTI instruction.
   B. An SWI instruction.
   C. An RTS instruction.
   D. An NMI instruction.

Unit 7 Examination

Interfacing — Part 1

1. A 3-state logic gate:
    A. Has an enable/disable input as well as the normal data inputs.
    B. Is effectively disconnected from the circuit when it is disabled.
    C. Is generally used when two or more gates drive the same bus line.
    D. All the above.

2. Which of the following lines or buses is bi-directional?
    A. The read/write line.
    B. The address bus.
    C. The data bus.
    D. All the above.

3. Which of the following lines or buses is an input to the 6800 MPU?
    A. The address bus.
    B. The $\phi2$ clock.
    C. Valid Memory Address (VMA).
    D. Bus available (BA).

4. The MPU can be stopped by external hardware by:
    A. Forcing the $\overline{\text{halt}}$ line low.
    B. Forcing the $\overline{\text{halt}}$ line high.
    C. Forcing the BA line low.
    D. Forcing the BA line high.

5. RAM places data on the data bus when:
    A. The positive-going edge of the $\phi2$ clock occurs.
    B. The negative-going edge of the $\phi2$ clock occurs.
    C. The positive-going edge of the $\phi1$ clock occurs.
    D. The negative-going edge of the $\phi1$ clock occurs.

6. In 6800-based systems, two control lines are generally connected to the address decoder along with the address line. These are:
    A. BA and $\phi1$.
    B. VMA and $\phi2$.
    C. TSC and $\phi2$.
    D. NMI and $\phi1$.

7. What is the minimum number of 256 by 4 RAM IC's required to develop a memory of 8-bit words?
   A. One.
   B. Two.
   C. Four.
   D. Eight.

8. The output of the address decoder normally connects to:
   A. The R/$\overline{W}$ line on the RAM IC's.
   B. The $\overline{CE}$ line on the RAM IC's.
   C. The $\overline{HALT}$ line of the MPU.
   D. The $\overline{NMI}$ line of the MPU

9. What type of circuit is required between the MPU data lines and the 7-segment display?
   A. A latch.
   B. A decoder/driver.
   C. An address decoder.
   D. All of the above.

10. Refer to the program shown in Figure 7-27 of the text. The number in accumulator A when the program starts is used as:
    A. The address of the corresponding 7-segment code.
    B. The 7-segment code.
    C. The offset address for the LDAA, X instruction.
    D. The address of the 7-segment display.

11. The program shown in Figure 7-32 of the text:
    A. Converts the 7-segment code in accumulator A into a serial bit stream acceptable to the latch.
    B. Converts the 7-segment code in accumulator A into a parallel data byte acceptable to the addressable latch.
    C. Converts the binary number in accumulator A into the corresponding 7-segment code.
    D. Loads eight addressable latches with the proper 7-segment codes to display an 8-character message.

12. An advantage of the circuit shown in Figure 7-33 of the text is:
    A. It requires fewer MPU instructions than the other methods of driving the display.
    B. It requires less MPU time than the other methods of driving the displays.
    C. It requires less external circuitry than the other methods.
    D. All of the above.

Unit 8 Examination

Interfacing — Part 2

1. In some microcomputer systems, input data from a keyboard is read repeatedly before it is accepted.
   A. This speeds up the MPU.
   B. This prevents two keys from being read at once.
   C. This overcomes contact bounce.
   D. All the above.

2. Refer to the program shown in Figure 8-5 of the text. Assume that key 6 is depressed. What hex number will be in accumulators A and B after the COMB instruction at line 18 is executed?

3. The purpose of the PIA is to:
   A. Simplify the problem of interfacing the MPU to the ROM.
   B. Simplify the problem of interfacing the MPU to the RAM.
   C. Simplify the problem of interfacing the MPU to input/output devices.
   D. Act as a universal input/output device.

4. The advantage of the PIA over conventional combinational logic circuits is:
   A. Generally, fewer IC's are required.
   B. The PIA is more flexible since its characteristics can be changed by the program.
   C. In many cases, the PIA requires no separate address decoder.
   D. All the above.

5. The A side of the PIA is selected when:
   A. RS0 = 0.
   B. RS0 = 1.
   C. RS1 = 0.
   D. RS1 = 1.

6. To select output register A of the PIA:
   A. RS0 must be 0 and bit 2 of control register A must be 0.
   B. RS0 must be 1 and bit 2 of control register A must be 0.
   C. RS0 must be 0 and bit 2 of control register A must be 1.
   D. RS0 must be 1 and bit 2 of control register A must be 1.

7. When the PIA is reset:
   A. Both sides are configured as outputs.
   B. Both sides are configured as inputs.
   C. The A side is configured as outputs while the B side is configured as inputs.
   D. The B side is configured as outputs while the A side is configured as inputs.

8. Refer to Figure 8-19 of the text. Which of the following sequences will cause display 4 to display the number 1.

   A. LDAA #01   B. LDAA #9F   C. LDAA #60   D. LDAA #10
      STAA 4004   STAA 4004   STAA 4004   STAA 4004
      LDAA #04   LDAA #10   LDAA #10   LDAA #04
      STAA 4006   STAA 4006   STAA 4006   STAA 4006

9. Refer to Figure 8-19 of the text. All displays can be blanked by storing:

   A. FF at address 4004.
   B. 00 at address 4006.
   C. FF at address 4004 and 00 at address 4006.
   D. Any of the above.

10. Refer to Figure 8-22 of the text. An indication that switch A is closed is:
    A. PB1 goes low when PB6 goes low.
    B. PB0 through PB4 are all high.
    C. PB1 goes low when PB6 goes high.
    D. PB0 goes low when PB6 goes low.